Walsingham

D0278423

Edited by Peter G. Cobb

White Tree
Books

First published in 1990 by White Tree Books,
an imprint of Redcliffe Press Ltd.,
49 Park Street, Bristol

© The authors and Walsingham College Trust

All rights reserved. No part of this publication
may be reproduced, stored in a retrieval
system, or transmitted, in any form or by any
means, electronic, mechanical, photocopying,
recording or otherwise, without the prior
permission of the publishers.

Typeset by Blackmore Press and printed and bound by WBC Ltd.

Contents

Foreword

This work is compiled almost entirely from articles and photographs which originally appeared in *Our Lady's Mirror* or *The Walsingham Review*. The *Mirror* was largely the work of Father Hope Patten. The first number came out in January 1926 and it stopped appropriately with his memorial number. The *Review* eventually took its place in 1961. The articles have obviously had to be edited but I hope I have not distorted their authors' meaning by doing so. Most of the early photographs were taken by Claude Fisher, the more recent by Ken Faircloth. I have included a few from other sources: I apologise if I have infringed anyone's copyright.

The value of this book lies entirely in the fact that it records the history of the shrine in the words of contemporaries. Only one set of *Our Lady's Mirror*, and that not complete, has been kept and it would be a great pity if its evidence should be lost.

The restoration of the Shrine of Our Lady of Walsingham and the ever increasing number of pilgrims to it is one of the most remarkable facts in the history of the Church of England in this century.

The Archbishop of Canterbury after his visit to Walsingham in 1980 wrote 'Walsingham has something to give to the whole Church and I look forward with enthusiasm to seeing growth in the next few years. A strong catholic evangelism needs a holy place for refreshment, renewal and re-dedication. Such Walsingham can become, not by fearful conservation, but by the courageous development of its own essential nature: a place where men and women come to a living faith in the incarnate Son of God, fostered by a right devotion to Mary his mother, within the sacramental community of the Church'.

Peter G. Cobb
Priest Guardian of the Holy House
Vicar of All Saints' Clifton

This design was drawn by a Walsingham artist, Lily Dagless, who, together with her brother James, made the original image at the Slipper Chapel in 1936.

Alfred Hope Patten
Priest
Restorer of the Shrine
1885–1958

Born at Sidmouth. Curate at Holy Cross, S. Pancras 1913–15, S. Alban's Teddington 1915 18, S. Mary's Buxted 1919–20, Good Shepherd, Carshalton 1920–21: Vicar of Great and Little Walsingham with S. Giles Houghton 1921–58.

How Fr. Hope Patten came to Walsingham

I was a boy when I went for a bicycle tour round the East coast en route for Painsthorpe, where I spent a couple of weeks with the Benedictines just before they went to Caldey.

In Norwich, looking up the route, I saw under the heading "Walsingham," "ruins of Augustine Priory; site of a mediaeval Shrine of the B.V.M." We decided to turn off our road and say some prayers on the site, but as we pedalled along, making for Peterborough, we decided "There isn't much to see there, by the book, and it's off the road; better leave it—perhaps get there some other time." And the very name of Walsingham was forgotten.

In 1914 I was a deacon in the Parish of Holy Cross, S. Pancras, where I had the great privilege of serving my title under Father F. E. Baverstock. One morning—I think it was at late breakfast—he brought a small figure of our Lady into the room to show me: a carved image with the Holy Child, and in her right hand a lily. "This," he said, "is going to Walsingham. There used to be a great Shrine of our Lady there. Father Reeves, the priest who gave me my title, has gone there." "Walsingham"—

5

where had I heard that name before? Yes, in school books. And then in a flash a dusty road in Norfolk and a discussion as to which road to take was vividly recalled. Again the name was forgotten.

About a year later I was at Buxted S. Mary's, and the parish priest. Father C. E. Roe, was showing me the church. "This chapel," he said, "was built by Father Wagner, and is the same size as the Holy House of Loretto, while the space within the screen to the east wall is the same length as the ancient Shrine that used to be at Walsingham." "Again that place—Ah yes! The ruins we nearly went to."

In 1920 I was offered a living in Norfolk, Little Walsingham! I went to visit the place at last. What a lovely-proportioned church, but oh! how bare! I shivered; but going up some steps into the old Guilds Chapel, there on a bracket on a pillar an image, neglected and forlorn—surely I knew that figure. Why yes! At once I was transported to the dining room in the basement of the Clergy House of Holy Cross, and there was Father standing by my side showing me this very statue of our Lady. And so I had come to our Lady's village after all, and here she was, having come on before. That was the turning factor—although at the time I did not really know it—which made me inclined to accept the benefice, although nearly three months elapsed before I took the plunge and said yes to the offer.

First Signs of the Revival of Devotion to our Lady of Walsingham

In the early 1880's Fr. Arthur Wagner, Vicar of St. Paul's Brighton, who had already built several churches in the town, decided to build one in Buxted. There seems to be no record of the reasons for his choice nor for the building, on the south side of the church of St. Mary, of a chapel whose measurements are those of the mediaeval Holy House of Our Lady of Walsingham.

Of this decision, Fr. Colin Stephenson wrote "A possible explanation is that Wagner was a great friend of Dr. Neale of East Grinstead, who was a great antiquarian and would almost certainly have followed the excavations at Walsingham in 1856 with great interest. It may well have been his influence which caused Fr. Wagner to make this gesture towards the ancient shrine of Mary in England."

Whatever the human explanation, St. Mary's, Buxted, and its 'Walsingham Chapel' were built and consecrated on St. Barnabas Day, 11th June 1887. There they stood, waiting for thirty years, until in 1917 Fr. Charles Roe arrived as Vicar. He had been curate to Fr. Halliwell, Fr. Wagner's successor at St. Paul's, Brighton, where he had come to know a young layman, Alfred Hope Patten. In 1919 he invited Hope Patten, now a priest, to be his curate at Buxted.

Now comes the part of the story which is, to those who hear it for the first time, the most astonishing. Fr. Roe of Buxted had a brother, Canon Gordon Roe, who was Rector of Blakeney and Rural Dean of Walsingham. In 1921 he wrote to his brother at Buxted asking him to suggest a suitable priest for the vacant living of Little Walsingham. Fr. Hope Patten's name was suggested, the living was offered and accepted, and he moved to Walsingham with results that need no telling here.

Michael Gudgeon

First Impressions

Arthur Bond remembers the induction of the "new Vicar"

It takes one back to those last years of the incumbency of "The Vicar", the Revd. E. L. Reeves, who at choir practice failed to appreciate my feeble efforts to sing the psalms of Dr. Woodward. I was therefore transferred to swell the ranks of the altar servers and became "boat boy" to Mr. H. Vaughan Hayler's "thurifer" when incense was first introduced at St.Mary's.

I recall attending the funeral of the last Lee Warner Squire and the viewing day at the Abbey sale. There I viewed with awe the lace collar said to have been worn by Charles, King and Martyr, on the scaffold at Whitehall before his execution. Although I did not then realize it, this could be said to mark the end of a Walsingham epoch. The beginning of the new was of course the Induction of the Revd. Alfred Hope Patten and I well recall the impressive mien and golden voice on this occasion, and the subsequent two Sunday evenings when he "read himself in". I remember too the enthusiasm aroused in us when Tommy Tapping, Fortescue in hand, drilled both Fr. Patten and the rest of us in the correct decorum of the sanctuary. Another highlight was the occasion when I attended Fr. Patten as cope-bearer for the Easter Procession singing "Hail Festal Day" when the magnificent Clints Cope was I suppose first used.

Reeves was vicar, 1904–20, Woodward 1882–88. Tapping was one of the young men who came to Walsingham with Hope Patten and lived in the vicarage. He later became Headmaster of the Sanctuary School. 'Fortescue' is Adrian Fortescue's book "The Ceremonies of the Roman Rite Described".

Fr. Derrick Lingwood Remembers

A fire in the Oxford Store Inn which I could see from the house in which I was born is my first recollection of Walsingham, and during the 1914/18 War of a Zeppelin coming over the house and dropping bombs not far from the village. Our Vicar, in his enthusiasm to give thanks for victory, caused the church bells to be rung before the official announcement had been made, and for this he was brought to the local Court, which sat and still does sit in Walsingham on the first Monday in each month, where he was fined, much to the annoyance of the parishioners.

The pattern of our worship seemed at this time to be an eight o'clock service on Sunday, followed alternately by a Sung Eucharist or Solemn Mattins. I used to go with my mother to Evensong, and because of my regular attendance I was asked to sing in the choir. When Fr. Reeves decided to leave Walsingham the services were taken by a different priest each Sunday, coming mostly from Norwich. One priest, after having said the Last Gospel to himself while the congregation sang a hymn, left the altar before the end of the hymn; we thought this very High Church and most reprehensible.

It was a long time before we could get a new vicar: many came to look but turned it down. The living at this time was in the hands of the Lee-Warners, and when it seemed almost hopeless to get anyone to become vicar of Walsingham because of its small stipend and three churches, the previous incumbent asked a past colleague of his, Fr. F. E. Baverstock, if he knew of anyone. Fr. Baverstock had at one time had a Fr. Hope Patten as his deacon and curate, and knowing that this young priest had a great devotion to the Mother of God he recommended him. From early childhood Our Lady had been an especial friend of this young priest, and at his ordination he

7

had prayed that when he was offered a living he might be offered a church which had for its patron the B.V.M. And then he was offered Walsingham. The difficulties were enormous, and he was three months making up his mind. At last he decided to leave the matter to the head of the Cowley Fathers at Oxford, and so he went to seek an interview; when he got there he was told that the Superior was conducting a retreat and could not be seen. This, thought Fr. Patten, was his answer. The good Fathers gave him some tea, and at the end of the table was a priest who seemed to resemble the Superior so closely that Fr. Patten asked who he was. The reply came: it was the Superior, who had had to come into the house on a business matter. Fr. Patten tackled him and was told: "I am in the middle of conducting a retreat: there is no time now." Again this looked like an answer, and he would not have to undertake this impossible task: a great weight seemed to be lifted from his shoulders. But as he was taking his leave the Superior sent a message saying: "Tell that priest to walk with me to the station; we can discuss things as we go," and as they walked through the streets of Oxford the Cowley Father heard all the pros and cons, and without a moment's hesitation said, "You will send a telegram accepting."

And so we had a new vicar, and in those early days what a vicar he was! With his good looks and charming personality he was a welcome visitor in every house, and at that time he was a persistent visitor. The services, the Calendar, his teaching, were all based on the Book of Common Prayer, and he set himself out not only to win the village people for Christ but also the neighbouring clergy. This he did by organising conventions, and the local clergy were invited to the Vicarage for the inside of a week at a time, and such excellent teachers as Fr. A. H. Baverstock and Fr. Monahan (later Bishop of Monmouth) expounded the Faith. The servers and choir were invited to the Vicarage every Friday evening, and the village was electrified by the rags which we had in the house and grounds. I was taken out of the choir at this time and made a boat-boy as it was said I made the other boys sing out of tune! It was not many months before the Blessed Sacrament was reserved in S. Mary's: at a later date, when the Bishop of Norwich maintained that Reservation was forbidden in the Diocese, being in his view illegal in the Church of England, Fr. Patten replied: "From my earliest days I have never lived in a place where the Blessed Sacrament was not reserved; since I have been a priest I have never worked in one without it, and now that I am an incumbent I would not." Nothing more could be said of this unless the Bishop wanted a head-on collision, which apparently he did not.

Also, as soon as our new priest arrived he was making enquiries at the British Museum about the ancient image of Our Lady of Walsingham, and on seeing a copy of the seal of the Priory which depicts the image, he decided to have a facsimile carved and set up in the Lady Chapel of the parish church. This was carved by a Carmelite nun. On July 6th of the year following his induction all was ready for the blessing and the first stage in the restoration of the Shrine. Many of the local clergy were there and a number of parishioners when Fr. A. H. Baverstock blessed the image and it was set up on its bracket looking towards the Priory from whence the original one had been taken away in 1538. Fr. Archdale King preached the sermon (this priest has since changed his allegiance; he is the author of many learned books on the different rites of Christendom).

After the setting-up of the image, had to come the first pilgrimage. This was organised by the old League of Our Lady. The secretary had had very little experience in organising pilgrimages and it would appear that any person writing for particulars was listed as intending to make the pilgrimage, with the result that Fr. Patten was told to expect forty people. At that time the only place for feeding was at the Black Lion and meals were ordered there; beds were provided in the village houses, and the great day arrived. The Parish Priest of Walsingham, with a few parishioners, went to meet the train in great excitement, and imagine their surprise when there stepped out of the train a very tall priest and a small woman.* "Where are the other thirty-eight pilgrims?" everyone exclaimed. The reply came: "We have not seen any others: as far as we know, we are the pilgrimage!" But even here the hand of God could be seen: Fr. Patten went round to his parishioners and said: "Forty pilgrims were expected, food has been provided, it must not be wasted; you must make the pilgrimage." Thus the idea and experience of pilgrimage was brought back to Walsingham people.

The next thing was to get Sisters working in the parish and to get a hospice for pilgrims opened when occasion offered. Mother Sarah of Horbury, where the Convent of S. Peter then was, saw the possibilities at Walsingham and sent three Sisters (I believe it was) and they took up their residence in the Vicarage Cottage. At first of course they were received by us villagers with suspicion, but among their number was a saint, Sister Veronica, and she, together with Sisters Grace Helen and Marguerite, soon won our hearts. It was not long before the Sisters moved into 'The Beeches' in Holt Road, changing its name to the Hospice of Our Lady. This house, besides one in Knight Street (later called S. Augustine's), some old cottages and a barn came into the market and these were bought by Mr. William Milner, as he then was. The old barn, later the pilgrims' refectory, had been used as a Salvation Army Citadel and at the time the property was acquired it was a Friends' Meeting House. Many letters passed between the Bishop of Norwich and the "Friends," as they were not particularly pleased to be asked to vacate the property.

In the beginning of the restoration of the pilgrimage the week-end gatherings had not then become popular and the yearly pilgrimages consisted of two two-day midweek pilgrimages, one organised by the League of Our Lady and one by the Catholic League, with perhaps a local one from Norwich towards the end of the year. On the Wednesday evening of those two pilgrimages, Bishop O'Rorke would always come over from Blakeney to sing Pontifical Vespers, take part in the procession round S. Mary's Churchyard and give Benediction. These 'goings-on' attracted people from far and wide and the procession was witnessed by hundreds from the surrounding villages. After the service Bishop O'Rorke went into the Pilgrims' Refectory and each pilgrim was presented to him. The restoration of devotion to Our Lady of Walsingham was helped enormously by this good Bishop; he had a great love of Our Lady and he backed up Fr. Patten's work in every way. The Bishop of Norwich went so far as to ask him to stop going over to the pilgrimages at Walsingham and told him "They only want you because you are a Bishop; if you were just a parish priest you would not be invited." To which Bishop O'Rorke replied: "Be that as it may" and said, "that Almighty God had magnified Mary and he proposed to follow His example".

During the central day of the two-day pilgrimage a tea-party was always given by Fr. Patten on the Vicarage lawn, and in those leisurely days the pilgrims were charmed by his sense of humour and by the certainty of his vocation to restore some of the glories of Walsingham, which he communicated to all.

During the Prayer Book controversy many Priests' Meetings were held in Walsingham and I learned much from the discussions which I was allowed to attend as a layman. At that time the Bishop of Norwich was a frequent visitor to the Vicarage as he too was violently opposed to the proposed Prayer Book, only from a different point of view. I remember thinking what strange bedfellows they made. Dr. Pollock said jokingly afterwards that he and Fr. Patten were instrumental in getting that book rejected.

* Elsewhere Fr Lingwood says the priest was a Fr Head who eventually retired to West Runton. The woman was Constance Baily.

From 1922 to 1931 the restoration grew steadily and pilgrims and visitors came in increasing numbers. Many of the latter were shocked by what they saw and wrote and told the Bishop so in no uncertain terms. During one of the debates in the House of Lords when he was making a speech, someone called out: "What about Walsingham? Put your own house in order." Many famous people visited the Shrine in the parish church, including Dr. Hensley Henson, the Bishop of Durham. He wrote to the *Evening Standard* afterwards, saying that it was quite natural that Walsingham should once again become a place of pilgrimage, but he deplored the revival of pilgrimage as it brought crowds of both sexes together, which too often led to deplorable results! I remember he was very scathing about the Pilgrimage Hymn, which caused Fr. Patten much laughter. He wrote: "The pitiful rubbish of the Walsingham Pilgrimage Hymn could only be termed as a part of a pageant: as an act of religion it would be profane"!!

With all this going on the Bishop of Norwich felt he must do something about it. How mysterious are the ways of the Almighty! There is no doubt in my mind that God the Holy Spirit was using the Bishop to get the Holy House reconstructed. One day, then, the Bishop descended on the parish; we were all told to pray. The Bishop, after walking round the church, was heard to mutter "It is far worse than I thought" over and over again, and said that the services must be brought more into line with the B.C.P.; the Shrine of Our Lady, all the statues and the Stations of the Cross must go. Fr. Patten replied that in regard to the Shrine of Our Lady he thought he could meet the Bishop; he said the original shrine never was in the parish church—it was always in a church by itself and he would see if some friends of his could build a chapel to house the statue. But with regard to the other things, they were common to every Catholic church in the Diocese and he could not agree to do as the Bishop asked without calling a meeting of all the Catholic clergy in the Diocese. This, the Bishop thought, was not at all a good thing to do, and agreed that the other possibility had better be explored first.

So off Fr. Patten went to London and met several friends, and to them he put the situation. Could they lend £1,000 to rebuild in Walsingham a copy of the Holy House? They all agreed that it must be done and that they would lend this sum. Mr. Romilly Craze, the architect, was next consulted and he was instructed to prepare a plan of the Holy House from the dimensions of the old one, only this time it was to have two chapels at one end and a porch. While preparing this plan, he remembered the conversation he had had with Fr. Patten and his saying what a pity it was that there was not the money to build the covering chapel, using the measurements given by William of Worcester of the building which stood in Walsingham from 1061 to 1538. So he made a second drawing showing the Holy House with its covering chapel which would, he estimated, cost something over £2,000 to build. I remember so well these plans arriving (Sir William Milner was staying with us at the time) and all of us saying what a pity it was that there was not the money to complete this scheme. Next morning when we were having breakfast, Sir William said: "Pat, we must have that covering building and I will lend the money," to which Fr. Patten replied: "No, you must not do this: you may lose your money." I think this was the only time I remember Fr. Patten having to be pushed to do a thing; my life up till then had been spent in holding him back because of the lack of money and I often told him how tired he must get of my always putting the brake on, to which he replied with that winning smile of his, that it was necessary to have this restraint if we were to build solidly. Sir William had to become quite annoyed, saying: "Well really, Pat, it is my money and if I lose it I lose it, but it will not be lost." So the building was ordered and it was not very long before all this borrowed money had been paid back.

There seemed to be no difficulty about where to build as the obvious place was the kitchen garden of the Hospice; it was near to the Priory grounds. While the working drawings were being prepared Fr. Patten was praying that if it was God's will that this Holy House should again be built in Walsingham the same sign might be given as was vouchsafed to Richeldis namely water. So the site was trenched, and a few feet down we found a cobbled courtyard, which Fr. Patten and others maintained was the courtyard of the burial ground of the Augustinian Canons. During the digging of another hole the sign was given by the Almighty—water burst forth; the diggers had hit on a disused well, and on examination it was found to be of Saxon origin and had evidently been intentionally blocked with clay, and at the bottom of the well were found shoe-soles of apparently mediaeval pilgrims. Here indeed was the answer to prayer, and it was therefore decided to enclose the well in the new building.

Everything was ready on October 15th 1931, when it was blessed by Bishop O'Rorke. After he had sung the Mass in the parish church, the statue of Our Lady of Walsingham was solemnly translated to its new home amid the rejoicing of thousands of people. This indeed gave a great impetus to the revival, and from that time the week-end pilgrimage started to grow and before long this building was found to be quite inadequate to accommodate the pilgrims desiring to come, so again plans were got out for a large building at the west end. These plans were printed and left about at the entrance to the Shrine, and one day this bore fruit, for again at breakfast Fr. Patten thrilled us all by saying that in his post was a letter from a priest sending £4,500 odd towards the new building. Working drawings were commenced, and as these took shape so did the size of the building; there was no need now to persuade Fr. Patten to embark on the project, and in the end it cost over £12,000.

I need say nothing about modern developments; they are all well known. In this restoration Fr. Patten was fortunate indeed to be able to draw on so many willing helpers. In due time the Horbury Sisters, who had become the Sisters of S. Peter's, Westminster, gave way to the Sisters from S. Saviour's Priory, Haggerston who, encouraged by Fr. Patten, have built their own Convent and Chapel. To the Sisters of whatever Order, Fr. Patten was deeply conscious of the debt he owed.

One of the things which was very dear to his heart was the Children's Home, and during the War years this Home (transferred from S. Hilary, Cornwall during the troubles there) was housed in the Vicarage and he therefore came into very close contact with it. He was intensely interested in the children, particularly when it was time for them to go out into the world, and the majority of them returned to him often for help and advice.

I suppose I knew him better than anyone because I lived with him for nearly thirty-two years. It is to him I owe my priesthood; without him I could never have realised my vocation. Like all great outstanding men he had his great gifts and great failings. I remember an archaeologist staying with us, and one day he said: "I am sorry for you, my boy, living with a genius." He was a very kind man; he never told one of their faults, he just looked at one and that was enough. He never held an inquest; the look was sufficient. His was a very lovable nature: very shy and utterly genuine. I suppose his greatest failing was not being able to see another person's point of view; to him black was black and white white—there were no shades in between. In the working out of what he believed to be his vocation he was ruthless with himself and also, if they stood in the way of the fulfilment of that vocation, ruthless with others. He had no money sense whatever and yet he was a big enough man to hand over all his money matters to another and for many years he did not even see his cheque book from one year's end to another. Even to the day of his death I doubt whether he ever knew where his income came from or how much it was. If there had not been others to look after him he would have given every penny he earned away. My life with him was indeed a happy time, for the most part in complete harmony; latterly we drifted apart in our ideas, but for me there was always a great affection for him coupled with heartfelt thanks for all he did for me. I tried to repay this in a small way by staying with him for over twenty years as a priest. He was a wonderful companion to have a holiday with; his knowledge of buildings and shrines in Europe was wide, and as a young man I learned much from him on our journeys together. When I was ordained, that pleasure had to be denied us as one or other of us had to hold the fort.

We who loved him can show our love by taking the work into which he put so much a stage further. The Church on Earth is poorer for his loss—I was going to say, the Church of England, but that would be only half the truth: he was not a Church of England man as such, his loyalty was to a wider conception of the Church, to the Catholic Church of Christ, to the Church of S. Hugh (his well-loved patron), and yet at the same time to the Church of S. Charles, King and Martyr. The Saints were very real people to him, and often when he had been exhausted with work and dropped off to sleep in his chair, those who were present would hear described in vivid detail such an event as the martyrdom of S. Thomas of Canterbury: but that is another story!

Parish priest, having received the pilgrims at the church steps, leads them into the church for the Parish Mass: October 14th, 1956, the Jubilee of the Shrine.

Reminiscences of Father Hope Patten

Sir William Milner

My first meeting with "Pat" as his friends were told to call him, was, I think, in 1923, at a League of Our Lady meeting in London, at which a young clergyman dressed in a frock-coat (Pat's usual London garb in those days) turned up to give a talk on the newly-reconstituted pilgrimage to Our Lady of Walsingham; and of absorbing interest it was. The result was that a small pilgrimage was made from London (very small it was too) in the autumn. It was to have consisted of three, I being one, but I went down with a bad chill, and only two made it. Next year, a large number came, and so it gradually continued to grow.

The inner story of how all this happened started a good many years earlier, when Pat, then still a boy, began to turn his thoughts to the priesthood, feeling a strong sense of vocation; and also a strong devotion to Our Lady. When his thoughts on the priesthood began to crystallise, he often asked Our Lady that, if he became a priest, he might go to some sphere of work that was particularly associated with her.

Fr. Lingwood has recounted how this all came about.

So Pat found himself Vicar of Walsingham.

Before he had been there many weeks, he determined that the Pilgrimage must be got going again; a lovely figure of Our Lady and the Holy Child, copied from the old seal of the Priory, was carved and coloured by a Religious, the figure that to-day stands in the Holy House; and it was solemnly blessed and enthroned on a carved bracket on a column of the Guilds Chapel in the ancient parish church of St. Mary, Little Walsingham. Here it remained until the new Shrine Church was built; and this Guilds Chapel was the centre of the early pilgrimages. At that time one of the highlights of the Pilgrimage was a visit to drink of the Wells in the Abbey grounds; and as these grounds were only open on a Wednesday, this meant that the pilgrimages could only take place between Tuesday and Thursday, a not very convenient time for many of the people who would otherwise have liked to come.

The typical form that the pilgrimages took at that time was as follows. The train was taken from Kings Cross to Fakenham, where the pilgrims were met by all sorts and kinds of conveyances, and driven the five miles to Walsingham. After being shown their lodgings at various houses in the village (where they were invariably received with the greatest possible kindness and attention by the householders), came the first visit to the Guilds Chapel, to fix their intentions, followed by Vespers of Our Lady, and supper, which in the very early days took place in a special room in the Black Lion, originally a mediaeval pilgrim Inn, which, so we are told, once welcomed Queen Philippa of Hainault during her pilgrimage here; for in the old days it was an understood thing that all, high and low, who could possibly do so, should come to Walsingham every year to salute Our Lady in England's Nazareth. This was followed by confessions in the parish church, always an understood thing at the commencement of any pilgrimage. And then, bed, lulled to sleep by the quiet voice of the trees. In the morning, priests on pilgrimage said their Mass, and the lay pilgrims made their Communion. After this came breakfast, and Stations of the Cross, and Sung Mass, followed by a somewhat strenuous walk (some 2 miles) to the Church of St. Giles at Houghton: and then over the footbridge over the Stiffkey to the Slipper Chapel, where in old days the pilgrims took off their shoes to walk barefoot the mile or so to England's Nazareth; the last to do so being Henry VIII, in the days before the Devil entered into him to destroy the Priory and all the other Religious Houses in the country. This Chapel was, in our early days, in repair but

14

unused. It had been bought some years previously by a lady, after being for years used as a hay shed. She unfortunately went over to Rome, and handed over the Chapel to the Benedictines. We used to visit it, and say some decades of the Rosary, before walking back to Walsingham, thinking I have no doubt of all the thousands that had passed that way before us, and feeling that so we were one of a great company that no man could number. After reaching Walsingham, and luncheon, we paid our sixpences at the old Priory gate in the High Street, and went into the ruins, seeing ahead of us the one noble arch that had formerly contained the great East Window of the Priory. After prayers at the site (as then supposed) of the Holy House on the North side of where the great church had stood, we went to the Wells, a hundred yards or so to the East of the Priory Church. Here, enclosed by a wall, and entered by a Norman arch moved from somewhere else, are two circular wells and a square piscina or bath, with steps leading down into it. We all drank of the water; and afterwards adjourned for tea on the Vicarage lawn, always a happy and festive occasion. Then came supper, Vespers of Our Lady and Benediction. And next morning, after Mass and a last visit to the Guilds Chapel to say farewell to Our Lady, we started on our various ways home.

Those were very happy days. Many came again and again, and we all felt like meeting old friends.

Not only was Pat immersed in the work of restoring the devotion to Our Lady of Walsingham: he had the Catholic way of life to build up in the three parishes. This he did partly by persistent visiting, getting to know his people, taking part in all their joys and sorrows, and getting them to trust and to love him. The work he did to spread Catholic faith and practice in these years is beyond all knowledge; at any rate, one measure of it was the usual attendance at the Sung Mass on Sundays, which, out of a population of some 1,000, was seldom less than 100–150; and the number of confessions was considerable, always the acid test of true conversion. He had a large band of local boys trained as Servers; and one of the joyous things of those times was the weekly servers' evening at the Vicarage, when Pat and all the rest used to play games, some of them on the riotous side! One often used to see him with an impish grin on his face, and his hair all upside down, as a result of some rough-and-tumble. I mention this, as it seems to me to set the whole tone and friendliness of the place.

Somewhere about 1926, he took up to the Vicarage a young chap from the village whom he thought had a vocation to the priesthood. This boy, as well as being convinced of his vocation, also developed a genius for finance, a quality lacking in Pat himself; and what Pat and the work and building up of the work of the Shrine owed to Fr. Derrick Lingwood (as he is now) is beyond all knowledge. Only a few intimates realised what it all meant; in latter years, Fr. Derrick was often down working at the Shrine Office until well after midnight; and it is entirely owing to the devoted work of Pat and himself that the work of the Pilgrimage is what it is to-day. Soon after he was priested by the late Bishop of Bradford, they started on an idea that Pat had long cherished, the beginning of a College of Priests founded on the idea of the ancient mediaeval Chantry Colleges. There were just themselves at first, and they made a chapel in the Vicarage in which they used daily to recite the Divine Office of Mattins and Evensong in common.

So things went on, gradually growing; until sometime early in 1930 the then Bishop of Norwich (Dr. Bertram Pollock) arrived in the parish, and asked to see the Vicar. He told Pat that he wanted to go down to the church. So down they went; and the Bishop marched along to the Guilds Chapel, where he surveyed all that was therein. The first protest was against the altar that was (and still is) placed in front of the Sidney Cenotaph. The Bishop said "What a pity to hide the base of it." Pat's reply was "But don't you think the upper part makes an admirable reredos to the altar?" This however did not satisfy my Lord, who wanted to see the base; so the frontal was lifted, and he crawled underneath; and the edifying spectacle was presented of the episcopal posterior protruding outside while the episcopal face was studying the monument! Afterwards he turned to the image: and he said "Mr. Patten, do you teach your people to worship the Virgin?" Pat replied "Yes, but only in the sense that you may say that you worship your earthly mother!" "Oh I see," said my Lord. He then moved closer to have a nearer look, and tripped heavily over the candle-box. "Oh, what HAVE I done?" said the Bishop, as candles shot in all directions. Anyway, the upshot of it was that the Bishop asked if the image might not be removed and be replaced by a picture of Our Lady (a subtle difference that seems to have been in vogue in the C. of E. for some years). Pat said he would have to consult his friends about this; and so they left the church. As they were going out, Pat asked for the episcopal blessing. Bertram seemed to be rather nonplussed by this, but finally said "yes": and solemnly led him up to the High Altar, and got behind the communion rails for the purpose. The upshot of all this was that the Bishop unknowingly started something of which he never dreamed, for Pat consulted with his friends and it was decided to accede to the Bishop's wish but to build, on some of the land already in the hands of the Shrine, a church modelled on the original lay-out of the old chapel: that is, the Holy House inside a covering church to which the image would be solemnly translated when it was finished. This apparently met with the Bishop's wishes (he had evidently been bully-ragged in the House of Lords by some of the backwoods Peers).

A charming picture of O.L.W. was painted by the late Clifford Pember, to take the place of the image. So the work on the new building was started, and the image translated on a morning of mid-October 1931. A large number of priests and lay-folk attended, to the number of a thousand or more. In the procession was also the then Abbot of Nashdom, and an Orthodox Archbishop. The procession stretched all the way from St. Mary's, along the High Street, to the new Pilgrimage Church. It was a colourful throng; the Archbishop in his eastern vestment with Deacons of Honour; the Abbot; various Religious, male and female, the donor of the land on which the new church was built carrying the title-deeds to be laid on the Altar of the Holy House; the image of Our Lady of Walsingham carried shoulder-high on a feretory carried by four priests in dalmatics, the Bishop of Accra, the consecrator of the new buildings, with his Deacons of Honour, and the Celebrant, Fr. Patten himself. It must have been a proud day for him. And then the image was installed in the Holy House in the niche where it still is over the altar. A strange thing happened the night before, when Fr. Patten was in the new building, and was conscious of the presence of several figures, in the dress of Augustinian Canons, visiting the various altars, consulting a paper which one of them held in his hands, and then nodding their heads in evident pleasure at each altar, newly consecrated that day. The vision remained for quite a time, and then faded.

Several interesting discoveries were made in the course of the building. When digging for the foundations, a cobbled yard was found some four feet below the surface; and beyond, the bases of walls, which seemed to agree very closely in plan and area with the dimensions left by William of Worcester and Erasmus. Furthermore, a well was discovered which, on being freed of the clay stopping, was found to contain at the bottom some old rusty knives and old shoes, which were pronounced by the Victoria and Albert Museum authorities to be of XVIth century date; and were evidently thrown in to dishonour the well. The water at once welled up again. The structure of the well was, at the bottom few courses, oak logs; and higher up circular, of rough flint-work; quite consistent with a late Saxon date: and near at hand was a large masonry foundation, square, and with a square socket in it, which was undoubtedly the base of a great cross. It was found that the well dropped into place exactly between two piers of the new arcade of the covering church; and we none of us have any doubts that what was discovered was the original Holy Well. This is still in use for drinking and sprinkling for pilgrims. The Stations of the Cross were built round the Hospice Garden, culminating in a Hill of Calvary carrying three great crosses; and also, for the XIVth station, a model of the Holy Sepulchre, containing an exact model of the Holy Tomb, and a figure of the Saviour lying in it.

All this meant a great stride forward for the pilgrimage; in the first place, now that we had our own Holy Well, and the probably original site of the ancient building, it was no longer necessary to restrict pilgrimages to Tuesday/Thursday; but they could be held on any days of the week. Parish pilgrimages began to come along from all over the country, besides many from the London area.

So the work grew rapidly, until by 1935 it became evident that the original buildings were quite inadequate to contain the numbers who came. One morning, when I was staying at the Vicarage, we were all at breakfast, when Fr. Derrick opened a letter that had come in the post, and casually pushed it over to Pat, saying "Here is a cheque for £6,000." Pat thought he was pulling his leg; but nevertheless it was true; and this amount made possible the much-needed extension to the Pilgrimage Church. The work was put in hand at the east end of the original building, which (the east end) was pulled down, and its site marked in the pavement by a line of grey bricks, and the arcades carried on to form a new nave and choir, with apse and various side-chapels, which brought the number of altars up to fifteen, one for each of the Mysteries of the Rosary. Care was taken in digging for the foundations of the new building, to look out for the old foundations, which were again found, all except one corner that came under the original building. They were carefully cleared, and the corner that came under the new extensions was crypted over so that it would be still possible to visit it.

I will not deal at length with the ensuing period, as many others besides myself have full knowledge of all that went on. I will just mention that, to ensure continuity, it seemed good to him to constitute a College of Guardians of the Shrine of Our Lady of Walsingham, part priests, part lay.

With the opening of the enlarged Pilgrimage Church, Fr. Patten and Fr. Derrick started to recite the Divine Office of Mattins and Evensong solemnly in the choir; and the Nuns had their own chapel behind the Organ Gallery, where is now a second vestry.

The work continued and grew until 1939 brought the Second World War; Walsingham became a Prohibited Area, and pilgrimages, except for those living actually in the area, had to cease, though the Guardians, as officials with official business there, were still allowed in. Later on in the war period, a part of the Quainton Hall School at Harrow was evacuated to Long Marston, in Northamptonshire. The Government eventually desired to commandeer the site where they were living, and it became necessary for the boys to seek a new home. Walsingham was chosen; and the derelict buildings in Army Yard, and also St. Augustine's, were altered, with Pat's inimitable genius for this sort of thing and now the Shrine had its own Choir School. After the War, he decided to make the Vicarage over to the School, and himself to occupy the buildings by the Shrine, which became the College of St. Augustine, originally intended for priests; but it so happened that several laymen wished to come, so the basis of it was changed to accommodate them. Pat and Derrick moved down there; it happened during one of my visits to Walsingham, and he and I spent the first night in the new Master's House. The Office of Mattins and Evensong were of obligation, and were solemnly and very beautifully sung, together with the Lesser Hours (the latter not at first of obligation).

All who have had the privilege of coming into the College will have been amazed by the charm that Pat got into those derelict buildings, and the charming gardens that he laid out both in the College Quad and later on in front of the buildings that were repaired for the accommodation of retired priests in what is now known as the North Wing.

But these are matters that are known to many others, who can deal with them far more ably than myself; all I will say is that, when Pat became a priest, the Profession of Architecture lost a very promising neophyte. Not that he had ever considered this as a possibility so far as I know. But he could have been a very great one.

The present Bursar, Stanley Smith, recalls the day Father Hope Patten died

Bells have a voice of their own, and how expressive this can be! That note of joy at times of happiness, or of alarm when danger threatens; and then the unmistakable tone of sadness at time of death. So it was in the late evening of 11 August 1958, that the pilgrims and villagers gathered in Walsingham were stunned with the news, that the Vicar, Fr. Patten, had died.

It was an historic day for another reason too, because it was the occasion of the first Episcopal pilgrimage to the Shrine and marked a new chapter in the history of England's Nazareth.

The day dawned bright and sunny and the last minute preparations went ahead quietly. At last all was ready and the visiting Bishops were welcomed to tea on the College lawn by the Guardians and those who work for the Shrine, with the Administrator acting as host as he had done on so many occasions. Having made their First Visit the pilgrims stayed for Rosary and joined in the Intercessions. After dinner at the Knight's Gate Café there was something of a panic to get vested in time for the evening torch-light procession. This followed the now familiar route and the grounds echoed with the sound of Ave, Ave, Ave, till having rescued the Shrine from "secular power" we returned to "see the honour of Mary restored". The

evening was hot and humid as if a storm was building up, in the Shrine the heat was intensified by the blazing candles; many of those in heavy vestments must have been uncomfortably conscious of this, but Benediction was given without incident. From photographs taken during the pilgrimage it is obvious that Father Patten was in pain, but he gave no sign at the time that he was in difficulty. The Host was then taken in procession to the Blessed Sacrament chapel, and it was perhaps fortunate that he was accompanied by servers, for having locked the Tabernacle and arranged the curtains he turned and collapsed.

In the past he had had many similar turns so we half believed him when he protested that everything was all right as we supported him back to the College. However, the Doctor advised him that it was serious and he needed complete rest. His reaction was quite predictable: "Impossible, there was the Bishops' pilgrimage to attend to", and for him there could be no delegation of this important duty. But his spirit was stronger than his body, and shortly after the doctor left he collapsed and died. The storm had passed.

The next evening the body was carried into the Shrine Church with the coffin open and Vespers of the Dead was sung: pilgrims and villagers filed past to

18

sprinkle Holy Water, so making a last act of homage to a dearly-loved and respected priest. Throughout the day priests had been arriving from all over England for the funeral, and the Holy Sacrifice was offered throughout the night. The following day, surrounded by the Guardians, Priests, and his faithful parishioners the body was escorted in solemn procession through the village to St. Mary's where he had laboured so devotedly for 37 years. The church was full to overflowing with those who had come from far and near to pay their last respects to this dedicated priest, whose work and influence had brought so many blessings. Without doubt all were deeply moved as he was laid to rest in a small grassy island alongside the west door, near Fr. Baverstock (under whom he had served his title) and William Frary, the Shrine beadle and gardener.

The funeral arrangements were complicated and detailed, yet all passed off without a hitch and just as he had himself directed: all the more surprising since these instructions were written in 1937 but not discovered until February, 1959.

He was always a controversial figure, uncompromising in his defence of the Faith, but utterly dedicated and convinced of his vocation. Perhaps his death was timely after all, for he might well have been overwhelmed by the wind of change gathering force at that time within the Church. However, his great work was not accomplished without sacrifice, but since it has prospered we can perhaps take this as a sign of approval: for "the Lord loveth a cheerful giver".

The Walsingham Friary

Father Hope Patten had a great interest in history and archaeology. He collected a mass of material for a history of the mediaeval priory in Walsingham, but he only managed to produce a sketchy Chronicle which appeared in instalments in Our Lady's Mirror *between 1936 and 1939. This article shows what might have been.*

All readers of the *"Mirror"* know something about the Priory of Our Lady of Walsingham, the great gateway of which abuts upon the King's Highway. The precincts of this Augustinian House were very extensive, stretching as they did from the Parish Church to beyond the site of the reconstructed Shrine to the north, all enclosed by a great wall.

Comparatively few, however, know of the even more interesting ruins of the Franciscan House to the south of the village, on the right-hand side of the road leading to Houghton-le-Dale, so that pilgrims who would naturally visualise the Canons of S. Austin in their white rochets and black cappas would possibly fail to include in their picture of Walsingham in the Middle Ages the familiar Grey Friar daily making his sandalled way through the throngs of pilgrims to the Holy House.

The Friars came to England during the lifetime of their holy founder, landing at Dover on September 10, 1224, at the very time when S. Francis of Assisi with the Brothers Masseo, Angelo and Leo were keeping the fast of S. Michael at La Verna. It was four days after their arrival in Kent that S. Francis received the Stigmata.

Doubtless this little band of Friars coming to England was much in the thoughts and prayers of S. Francis at that time, for had he not especially chosen their leader, the Blessed Agnellus of Pisa, to head this mission and to be the first Minister Provincial for our Island?

Accompanying him and doubtless appointed by S. Francis were: Friar Richard Ingworth, a Norfolk man of a neighbouring village to Walsingham; Richard of Dover;

Enid Chadwick's drawing of the friary.

William of Esseby, a Novice, another native of Norfolk, from Ashby in that County; Friar Henry, a Lombard; and Brother Lawrence of Beauvais, to whom S. Francis gave his own tunic, which became one of the precious Franciscan relics and was preserved at the London House in Newgate Street.

Walsingham was in the Cambridge Custody, in which there were nine houses at the Dissolution.

The House in Cambridge was founded the year after their coming to England in the lifetime of S. Francis. It stood where the present Sydney Sussex College is, incorporating as it does part of the House, but the first dwelling of the Cambridge Friars was lowly in the extreme, and we are told that the Chapel was so humble that one carpenter made it in one day. Only three Franciscans were sent to found this House in 1225. They were: Brother William, Brother Hugh (these were both clerics), and Brother Elias, a Novice, who was so lame that he had to be carried into Choir. Despite their small numbers they sang their Office solemnly. A characteristic of the Cambridge House was its remarkable poverty, and thirteen years after its foundation the brethren were so poor they still had no cloaks!

Many are the well-known names in Europe who belonged to the English Franciscans during the course of their history, and it is impossible to enumerate them. It is interesting, however, that a Friar of the Worcester House—Adam de Marisco—

20

became the Secretary of S. Anthony of Padua. One scarcely imagines this popular Saint being so attended!

The Friary at Walsingham was not founded for a hundred and twenty years after the Friars' first landing in England, and two hundred and eighty-six years after the building of the Holy House, and two hundred and seven years after the coming of the Austin Canons to the village.

No wonder, when it was first known that Elizabeth de Burgh, Countess of Clare, who held from her brother the Manor of Walsingham, intended to found a Franciscan House in Walsingham, that the Canons who had had full possession of the place for so long did everything in their power to prevent it, and perhaps not wholly without good reason, for remarkable privileges were granted to the Friars. From 1231 they had been, and still were, exempt from Episcopal jurisdiction; they were free to hear the confession of any parishioner where they settled, as well as others; they could bury in their Churches anyone who so wished, and were permitted to preach not only when they liked in their own Churches, but in the open streets and squares of the countryside. Besides, the site proposed by the Countess for her new foundation was at the very entrance to Walsingham, so that the vast majority of the pilgrims coming to visit the Shrine would be likely to be intercepted by the Friars, and there was fear of not only losing the gifts and offerings they had intended for the Holy House, but in the case of the better-to-do, their patronage and favour. It was also in those days no easy matter to keep the parish and other Churches in repair and to get the necessary funds for running them—any more than it is, *as we find to our cost*, in our days in great places of pilgrimage, hence the anxiety of the Canons, who held the livings of the Parish Church of S. Mary as well as S. Peter's. But all their efforts were in vain: appeal to Elizabeth de Burgh: appeal to the king and his good Queen Phillipa of Hainault, who was such a constant pilgrim to the Shrine and patron of the Canons: appeal to the Holy Father himself, were all of no avail, and on February 1, 1347, the Lady of the Manor received licence to found the House at Walsingham for twelve Friars under Royal and Papal sanction, and in 1348 the Friars were in occupation. It was always a very small foundation; the original grant only consisted of four acres one rood of land, but within twelve months this was found inadequate and the first Guardian of the House was licensed to acquire a further three acres adjoining the original grant.

Three years later permission was given to enclose and take in the way or road "leading from North Barsham to the Chapel of S. Mary in Little Walsingham" which ran "beneath" or close to the Friary, on condition that they constructed on their own ground a road of the same breadth and length which is that part of the way still leading to the south out of the village.

In 1425 Edward Mortimer, 5th Earl of March, gave them a close of three acres on the south of the Mansion of the Priory. There seems to have been trouble over this last gift, as it was forfeited, but finally granted to John Hakelying, the Warden of the Friars, by Henry VI, and at the same time he licensed the Duke of York to grant a cottage and another three acres and a garden containing one-quarter of a rood in Little Walsingham to the same Warden. The total possession of the Friars in Walsingham consisted of thirteen acres, one rood, ten perches.

John Hickeling (Hackelyng) was still Warden in 1430, when he was granted on January 21 a sum of £10—evidently in order to attend a General Chapel at Assisi in June of that year. This sounds uncommonly like a "Continental tour for £10," a book published in our own time, but one has to remember that this sum represented at least £250 to £300 in our present day values. Little is known of the contents of the Friary Church; there is mention of an Altar of S. Anthony, and a note that in 1514 Robert Grey of Walsingham gave two pairs of silver censers to the Friars (should these have gone to the Canons, or even the Parish Church?). The son of the local Rector, Laurence of Althorpe, of Thursford, gave a gift in 1375 and a few similar donations are recorded.

There is no mention of the effects of the Black Death, which was so deadly in this district, but the plague broke out in the year following the foundation of the House, 1348, and lasted until September, 1349. Indeed, the story of our Friars is hidden and forgotten, and there is scarcely a mention made of them from the time of their coming to the time of the Dissolution.

In 1535, Giles Coventry was the Guardian here, but three years later, at the time of the suppression of the House, he is found at the Reading Friary, and is one of the signatories of that place. In the same year, 1538, Walsingham Friary surrendered to Richard Ingworth, Suffragan Bishop of Dover. He wrote to inform Cromwell that most of the goods had been sold or pledged prior to his arrival and that there was little left of anything of plate, lead or implements. It seems the Church was demolished the following year, as there is a record that in 1539 the Guild of the Annunciation of Blessed Mary at Walsingham paid 40s. as part payment for the great bell of the Friars' Minor, this possibly is the big bell now in S. Mary's recast in Elizabeth's time.

Today there are still extensive remains of unusual interest, for they consist of the most complete example of the domestic part of any Franciscan House still extant in England. The site covers over two and a half acres and is enclosed on the north by cottages, a garden and chapel, which abut on to the market place and at one time evidently formed part of the precincts. On the west there is an ancient lane—Back Lane; to the south an open field, and on the east there is the road mentioned above; the whole is enclosed by a stone wall.

The chief entrance was doubtless from the market place, and a small cul-de-sac in the south-west corner evidently marks the site, as it also leads as usual in such foundations directly to the "walking place" of the Church, this "walking place" being a passage dividing the Choir of the Friars from the preaching nave of the laity, above which almost invariably was the tower for the single Church bell. Near here was the anchorite's hole or cell.

There was a postern, without doubt, on the roadway, at one or other of the present entrances, near to which the lodging of the Guardian of the House stood, possibly adjoining the little cloister. Nearly all of the Church has vanished, part of the external walls remain and some of the foundations, covered, are still extant. The enclosing walls of the great cloister to the south of the site of the Church remain, and the foundations of the Chapter House abutting on the east side.

William of Worcester gave the dimensions of the Church: the nave 94ft. x 56ft., the Choir 87ft. x 30ft.; the walking space has been found to be 11ft wide interiorly x 28ft. The total length arrived at by recent excavations make the Church 198ft. long.

The bricks used among the flint work are said to be of a hard wrought type with straw-marked bed, in use in Norfolk throughout the 14th and 15th centuries. The great cloister is 108ft. east to west and 99ft. 6in. north to south.

The Refectory stood on the first floor, over the south walk of the great cloister and the north walk of the little cloister. The little cloister is a beautiful ruin, and contained the kitchen and other departments of a similar nature. The remains of what are considered to be the kitchen with a hatch are to the west of the cloister, and to the west of the great cloister is a large building believed to have been the Guest House.

Here, in the beautiful remains, is housed part of the Sanctuary School, forming a second house, that of S. Francis! May the Saints of the Order look kindly on the present occupiers of the Friary and the Saints intercede.

On writing about Fr. Hope Patten

For over six months I was actively engaged in writing a book which is being published by Darton, Longman and Todd, in October 1970 under the title of *Walsingham Way*. I have tried to make it a simple account of what we know of the foundation and history of the Shrine of Our Lady at Walsingham both before and after the Reformation.

It is surprising how little has really come to light on the historical side and there are many things which we should like, but probably will never know.

Over half the book is concerned with the restoration of the Shrine and so is bound to be more or less a biography of Alfred Hope Patten, who made it his life's work.

To write this I have had to read a lot of letters, and those who ever received one from Fr. Patten will know how difficult it was to decipher his handwriting, but there was also a vast amount of other material to digest.

I knew Fr. Hope Patten well in his later years so that it was fascinating for me to be able to get glimpses of him as a boy and as a young man. In many ways he was a very consistent character for many of his early enthusiasms, such as for heraldry and hagiography, he retained to the end of his life.

If one is writing about someone one has known well, admired and loved, there is a great temptation to overlook their faults and present them rather like a "touched-up" photograph. I have tried to resist this biographer's snare, which is not ultimately sympathetic to the character about which one is writing for it is apt to ring false. We all have our faults and they are part of the real person, and the things we manage to accomplish in spite of them is the encouraging story of a man's life.

Father Patten had faults and limitations, but I think the great encouragement of the Walsingham Story is that he restored the Shrine and left the legacy that he did in spite of all.

Founders have to have a very special temperament or they could not get things done. They have to be single minded and rather ruthless if any one gets in the way and above all they need tenacity. All these things are exhibited in Fr. Patten and he certainly was a true Founder.

It is easy to look back and see what ought to have been done, but he was in the thick of a battle and there is no doubt that if he had not been prepared to fight the restoration would have remained a pious hope.

He was convinced that the moment he died there was a danger that everything would come to an end, and to prevent this he felt that he must plan ahead for dangers which in the event have never taken place.

It was sad to read the many letters which he wrote full of forebodings about the future, and to see the enormous efforts he made to found a religious community, which he thought the only possible way of establishing continuity. Like many great men he died with something of a sense of failure. And yet the work which he began continues to grow and has become integrated in the Diocese and the Church of England in a way which he might have found difficult to believe possible.

There is also great fun and gaiety in his life as he gathered around him amusing and eccentric people, and he had an amazing gift for lighting up other people with his own enthusiasm.

The period of his life which most fascinates me in his early years at Walsingham in the 1920s when he displayed his astounding Pied Piper gift in getting a whole Norfolk village to dance to his tune. It was a real work of conversion as exciting as any in the annals of the Catholic Revival in this country. He said later in life that he was conscious of an inspiration at that time which faded away as the Shrine and the Pilgrimages began to get established.

So much has happened in the Church since he died that I constantly say to myself "what would Fr. Hope Patten have thought?" There is a notice somewhere in the sacristy which used to be on the notice board, asking people not to join in when Mass is being said! I think he would have disliked many of the "new things", but he had a great veneration for the Holy See and I believe that he would have been prepared to "go along" in spite of his personal feelings.

I like to remember him on Whit-Monday sitting on the wall at the top of the steps from the Sacristy, as I have so often done myself. Crowds of people around the Holy Well, the constant sound of the Stabat Mater as parties made the Stations of the Cross. All these things had been carefully planned in his fertile mind and here they were alive and in use, and one could sense his feeling of satisfaction. I like to remember him also sitting by the log fire in his room and telling one of his plans for the future in such a way that one was caught up oneself in the vision which he had.

It has been a privilege to write about him and to have experienced both his joys and his miseries in the records he has left, but it is encouraging to have lived long enough to see that his work is bearing fruit according to the promise of the good seed.

Colin Stephenson.

The Restoration of the Shrine

Fr Hope Patten looked back over twenty five years in 1947

The present Incumbent of Little Walsingham had been in the parish a little over a year when an old priest from a neighbouring parish, who was then in his late seventies, came over to see him and said: Some of us Clergy in the neighbourhood are very worried and anxious about what you are doing at Walsingham and the Anglo-Catholic Movement. Will you explain it to us? His reply was that being the baby of the district he wouldn't presume to do that but he would gladly invite those who were interested to come to Walsingham and he would get a competent priest to give a series of instructions. The result being that nine clergymen stayed for the inside of a week in July of that year, 1922, and Fr. Alban Baverstock came to deliver the instruction on the faith while the parish priest acted as Devil's Advocate and put objections and asked questions, as the guests were too shy for the first couple of days to ask anything. The days commenced with Mass in S. Mary's Church; breakfast; "quiet time"; then sitting round the dining room table, Conference; after lunch, tennis, bowls, etc.; Evensong and Simple Benediction at 6 o'clock and after supper a second conference and the days ended with Compline. The results were really surprising, and a great advance was made in the teaching and practice of the parishes in which these priests had charge. Most of them have now departed this life—may they rest in peace.

It was during these conferences, towards the end of the week, that the new image of Our Lady of Walsingham, having been made from the seal of the Priory and accounts culled from the British Museum and elsewhere, was placed in the South Porch of the Parish Church, and on the evening of July 6th was blessed after an oration delivered from the steps of the font. A procession was formed consisting of inhabitants from the village, the visiting priests, girls in white, some carrying long boughs of syringa and others bearing the feretory on which the image was placed, accompanied by the organ and the ringing of the old bells in the Church tower. "O.L.W." was carried up into the Guilds' Chapel of S. Mary's and there enthroned on the pillar to the south of the Altar.

From that day forward each evening, with the exception of Friday and Saturday in Holy Week, the Rosary has been said before the Image and after a few days, not more than a week after the setting up of the figure, an intercession book was opened and petitions offered, also daily. These have now amounted to hundreds of thousands of requests.

Pilgrimages commenced, led by the then League of Our Lady, now known as the Society of Mary. The Catholic League was next in the field and has ever ranked foremost in devotion to Our Lady of Walsingham.

Wonderful answers to prayers were noticed almost at once and during those early years miracles were performed at the intercession of Our Lady, and these have continued to follow the prayers of those who seek her aid before the throne of her Divine Son. The Society of Our Lady of Walsingham was inaugurated in 1923 when a number of people belonging to Walsingham joined, these for the most part remaining loyal members of the Society. A number have already departed this life. The Society is for pilgrims, those who themselves have visited the Shrine and who promise to help to make known the devotion and to spread the knowledge of England's Nazareth.

During the first nine years the work was much helped and encouraged by the loyal and loving support of Bishop O'Rorke, at that time Vicar of Blakeney, to which parish he had gone after resigning his See. Pilgrims of the early days can never forget his devout sermons, his patient calm during the long Pontifical Vespers or Masses, and the processions around the outside and inside of the Church which used to be packed with pilgrims and visitors and village folk. The revival at Walsingham owes very much to this steadfast friend and true client of the Mother of God.

In the early days of 1931 the Bishop of the Diocese, Doctor Pollock, became disturbed at the developments and the continuance of the devotion in the Parish Church. People had evidently been "getting at him," as it is said. Talks followed between the Bishop and the Parish Priest, which resulted in the latter going to London and getting friends to promise to guarantee certain monies. Having got that assurance, the discussion ended by his going to the Palace and informing the Bishop that he intended removing the Image of Our Lady of Walsingham from the Parish Church and putting a substitute in its place. He was able to do this as the Shrine had never originally occupied St. Mary's. In reply to the Bishop's question "But what are you going to do with it?" he said "Build a wayside Chapel to contain the statue of Our Lady of Walsingham!" And so the matter ended.

Bishop Bertram Pollock had been, and remained to the end, always a very kind and considerate friend to the parish priest and their relations were always, even when sometimes they were certainly very strained, both gracious and even affectionate. The revival owes much to the Bishop of Norwich for his patience and Christian toleration. May he have his reward.

On S. Theresa's day, October 15th, 1931, considerably over three thousand pilgrims assembled at Walsingham. Mass was pontifically sung by Bishop O'Rorke in S. Mary's Parish Church and Fr. Alban Baverstock preached. In the afternoon, after an oration by Father Ernest Underhill, Benediction of the Blessed Sacrament was given and then the procession set out for the reconstructed Shrine. The gathering included Religious, representatives of Guilds and Societies, over one hundred and fifty vested priests, Abbot Prideaux of Pershore and Nashdom, as well as Bishop O'Rorke.

Arrived at the newly constructed Holy House, the Image was set up in its niche over the Altar. At the conclusion of the ceremonies the pilgrims filed through the Chapel.

It was the beginning of the second chapter in the story of "the return of Our Lady to Walsingham."

It wasn't long before it was discovered that the Holy House, with its small covering building was totally inadequate for the crowds that began to make the pilgrimage. This was doubtless increased by the discoveries which had been made when the new building was in the course of construction. Remains of an ancient cobbled yard and the foundations of some mediaeval building were found some four feet below the ground and also a well packed with clay and, at the bottom, soles of shoes of the early or middle 16th century and other articles of that period.

The distance, too, from the Parish Church, where the pilgrimage services had to take place on account of the space required, all helped to make it evident that a larger building would have to be put up sooner or later.

A brochure was printed stating the needs and within a short time the money was coming in in such a way as to make it seem safe to go forward with the plans put out by the architects, Messrs. Milner and Craze, who had so ably designed the first buildings. The result was the erection of the Pilgrimage Church, with its Chapels in honour of the fifteen mysteries of the Rosary surrounding the Holy House. Most of the Chapels were erected, or at least furnished, by various societies, foremost being the Confraternity of the Blessed Sacrament, the Seven Year Association*, Society of Our Lady of Walsingham, Society of Mary, Priest Associates of the Holy House, Chantry Chapel of Frs. Tooth and Wilmot Phillips, the Fynes-Clinton Chantry and Catholic League Chapel, the Milner Chapel, etc.

The year following the blessing of the new church saw over thirty-two thousand pilgrims and visitors at the Holy House, and then came the war. Those dark and frightful nights, when almost without exception after the enemy aircraft started crossing our coast line they moaned over the Stiffkey Valley, constantly dropping bombs in places around the Sanctuary. Every village was damaged by the enemy

---

* The Seven Year Association was a youth organisation under the auspices of the Church Union, set up in 1933.

Bishop Mowbray Stephen O'Rorke, Bishop of Accra 1913–24 and Rector of Blakeney 1924–35. He died in 1953 and his ashes were buried in the Shrine.

27

except Walsingham. By day they came over—hedge-hopping outside the Vicarage. Often and often, whilst Rosary was being said in the winter evening, the shrapnel would rattle on the roof and the Church rock like a ship at sea. But within the Shrine there was always a wonderful peace and calm—Our Lady's Mantle was spread over it.

Peace came and pilgrimages of thanksgiving were made. A scheme has been put out for a substantial memorial of our gratitude to God and Our Lady for her prayers in the form of the north walk of the cloister with a memorial chapel at right angles to it and a large room over the cloister walk, to form a library, but so far little enthusiasm has been shown for this memorial at England's National Shrine of Our Lady.

July 5th to 12th of this Jubilee Year—1922-1947—was in many ways a wonderful week at Walsingham. The celebrations commenced on the Saturday and continued throughout the octave. The Pilgrimage Church was decorated, as is our custom on high feasts, and for this occasion wreaths of evergreen hung from and down the campanile within the windows of which lights were kept burning throughout the nights.

High Mass was sung each day in the Pilgrimage Church, with the exception of Sunday when, of necessity, it was at the Parish Church. Solemn Benediction was given each day in the Sanctuary Church. Various pilgrimages were made during the octave and on the Wednesday evening a social gathering was held for the inhabitants of the village who are especially identified with the Shrine. On the Saturday a number of pilgrimages from various parts of the country came to Walsingham, including one organised by the Church Union led by the Secretary, Fr. Riley.

And so the first twenty-five years of the story of the restored Shrine of Our Lady of Walsingham has passed. Thousands have trod the pilgrims way; innumerable prayers and vows have been offered; and "showers of blessings," both spiritual and temporal have been granted by heaven in response to their petitions and Our Lady's intercession.

Father Hope Patten described the shrine as it was being built. He himself claimed that the 'plans were prepared. . .upon the sketch and dimensions furnished by the Parish Priest.'

In a garden divided from the ruins of the Augustinian Priory by a narrow road cut, it is believed, subsequently to the dissolution, the new chapel of the Blessèd Virgin Mary, containing the re-constructed Holy House of Walsingham, is gradually rising.

From excavations made during the preparation of the site it was discovered that this garden once formed part of a courtyard, and it is considered by the architect and other experts to have been part of the original Chapel yard of the ancient Shrine.

After the position of the new buildings had been determined a thirteenth century well was unearthed on a level with the court, some four feet below the surface. As it was cleaned a fresh and cold spring bubbled into the old well. Among the rubbish taken out several soles of early fourteenth century shoes were found together with some pieces of mediaeval pottery, &c. It was found necessary either to re-close this well or incorporate it in the Chapel, and it was determined to follow the latter course.

The Sanctuary of Our Lady of Walsingham will consist of an outer building called by William of Worcester and subsequently the "Novum Opus" or "New Work"; this will be of the same dimensions as the original, forty-eight feet long by thirty feet broad. It consists of a narrow nave separated from even narrower aisles by a double

The Shrine of Our Lady in Parish Church before 1931.

row of five slender pointed arches. At the West and behind the altar will stand the Holy House (23ft–6 × 12ft–10), as the Santa Casa at Loretto is to be seen to-day, and very similar to it—as the original Shrine was always supposed to have been a copy of the House in Nazareth, where the Incarnation took place, which house is now venerated at Loretto.

Erasmus tells us that entrance and exit to the Shrine was by two doors facing each other; so it will be again, and one small window in the West will, as at Nazareth, be the only provision for light, except from the open doors.

At the East will be the altar and image of Our Lady of Walsingham.

29

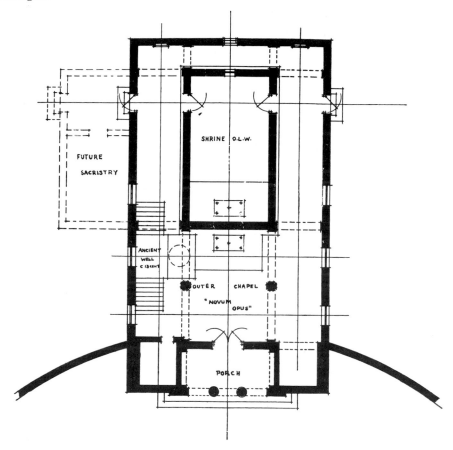

The whole outer building will be covered by a high pitched roof covered with red pantiles.

To the "Novum Opus" our architects have added a porch and two chapels at the main entrance opening out into a small court abutting on Knight's Street and opposite to the present re-constructed Knight's Gate.

The garden of the Sanctuary is to be converted into a Pilgrims' Park, and a Via Dolorosa is being formed which will cross the Hospice gardens.

The direction of these Stations follows the same course as the original Way of Sorrows in Jerusalem. Starting from the East it goes due West, and then, turning South, for a short distance proceeds due West to Calvary. As, too, at Jerusalem, so here the fourth Station, "Jesus meets His Mother," is represented by a little Chapel, here known as the Chapel of *Our Lady of Sorrows**. Stations 10, 11, 12, 13 on the "hill" in the West are arranged in the same position as Calvary in the Church of the Holy Sepulchre.

To the North-West in "a garden" is the 14th Station, which consists of a reproduction of the outer and inner chambers of THE HOLY SEPULCHRE. This tomb is the exact size of the actual burial place of Our Lord: 7ft. long by 6ft. wide

---

* Stations 3 and 4 had to be moved, and the original chapel demolished when the Shrine Church was built.

'Over the Holy House was built a protecting chapel.'

and 6ft. high, and contains a figure of the dead Christ. Leaving the tomb to the right of the Altar in the outer Chamber is an image of the Risen Lord proclaiming His victory over death.

31

West Entrance to the Shrine of Our Lady before additions in 1938 showing the original campanile over Station 4.

The opening of the restored shrine 1931

The ceremonies attendant upon the opening commenced on Saturday, October 10th, when our good friend, Bishop O'Rorke, came and Blessed and Baptized the peal of bells attached to the sanctuary. It was an unusual scene in English religious life of today, as the Bishop, anointing each bell with the Oil of the Sick and within with Holy Chrism, passed from one to the other.

On Thursday, October 15th, at 7 o'clock, a few parishioners and others assembled outside the Chapel and assisted at the blessing while the Priest passed round the outside of the building and aspersed it. Entering to the words of the Litany, the circuit of the Chapel was made within, and later aspersed, first on the Epistle side and then the Gospel. At the conclusion of the blessing a votive Mass (with Gloria and Creed) was said of the Annunciation, being the fitting Mass on such an occasion as the opening of the Holy House—England's Nazareth. The Mass proceeded in the ordinary way until the offertory, when just before the oblations were brought to the Altar, Sir William Milner, who gave the site on which the Sanctuary has been built, came forward and presented the deed of conveyance to the Celebrant who laid it on the Altar, where it remained until the lavabo, when he gave it into the custody of Fr. Fynes Clinton, who held it on behalf of the other trustees during the Mass. Sir William then served the lavabo, an ancient privilege accorded to the donor of lands on which a chapel or church or monastery was founded.

At 11.30 there was High Mass at the Parish Church, at which Bishop O'Rorke

'The Translation of Our Lady of Walsingham' October 15th, 1931. Sir William Milner is on the left.

pontificated. The sermon was preached by that veteran champion of the Catholic Revival, Fr. Ernest Underhill, of S. Thomas's, Toxteth Park, Liverpool. He said:

> They were going to do that which in God's good time would help to spread more and more the devotion of Catholics to the Blessed Virgin Mary and above all to the Incarnation of her divine Son. Men of his age, said the preacher, looked back to the history of seventy or eighty years of the movement, and they saw that God brought forth the old treasures of the Catholic Faith, and was presenting them to the generation in which they lived. Some of them used to think that they were lagging in the presentation of the whole of the faith. But it seemed, as he looked back, that it was in God's mercy that things should go a little bit slowly. As he looked back and remembered the first glimmers of the Catholic faith, it seemed that Mary was hardly known then. There were, however, certain great things which their forefathers taught them about the Real Presence and the Sacrament of Penance. As time swept on, more and more of Catholic truth came back into the minds of men and women in the English Church. Our Blessed Lady began to take that rightful place in men's esteem which for all those years before the Reformation Mary had received. To-day they were going to do something which would help towards making the worship of our Lady of Walsingham no longer a parish matter, but something that would be national. That day they were taking her to the new sanctuary that was a copy of the Holy Home where was nursed the little Babe who was God Almighty. From henceforth Mary had come back into her own to show forth the incarnate life of her divine Son.

On the afternoon of that memorable day, the Parish Church was once more crowded to its utmost limit, when Fr. Alban Baverstock preached. Then the procession was formed for conveying the Image of our Lady to the new Shrine and setting it up in the place prepared for it.

Picture then a perfect Autumn day (I quote once more from *'Our Lady's*

The procession passing the Abbey Gate in High Street.

Mirror'. . .), with scarcely a breath of air stirring, the trees clothed in glorious tints, and in their setting of old Tudor Houses and low, red-roofed ancient cottages, a procession with over a thousand people walking, each bearing his or her lighted taper; many women in blue veils, little children in white casting their flowers; dark-habited religious, nuns and monks; over a hundred priests in cassock and cotta; the mitred Abbot of Pershore and Bishop O'Rorke. Behind streamed the many hundreds of other people, all singing the glories of Mary, and in the midst of this throng, high and lifted up upon the shoulders of four clergy in dalmatics, and under a blue and gold canopy fixed to the feretory, sat the venerated figure of our Lady, crowned with the silver Oxford Crown*, and robed in a mantle of cloth of gold.

Around the feretory walked men carrying torches; in front the lay guardians of the Shrine who were able to be present; and behind five of the priest-guardians, and immediately following them a group of banners from various parishes, and pilgrim banners. The procession passed between streets hung with flags and wreaths of flowers and evergreens, accompanied by singing and the chiming of the bells of the ancient parish church.

When the head of the procession, which was over half a mile long, arrived at the Court before the Sanctuary, the bells of our Lady's chimes rang out. The processionists formed up in semi-circular rows on either side of the Porch—first the women in veils, then the nuns, then the monks and clergy. Finally the Abbot and Bishop reached the entrance to the church before which rested the image of Mary surrounded by torches and her attendants. The Prelate intoned the Magnificat and incensed the Blessed Virgin, at the conclusion of which the feretory was again lifted up, and to the strains of the Salve Regina, passed into the Chapel and the Holy House.

Here it was enthroned in the niche prepared above the Altar. . . The function concluded with a Solemn Te Deum sung by all within and around the Shrine and those standing in the road outside. It took three quarters of an hour for the pilgrims and visitors to pass in quick succession through the Shrine without pausing.

Our Lady has come back to Walsingham.

Sermon delivered by Father Alban Baverstock in S. Mary's Church, Walsingham, on the occasion of the re-opening of the Shrine.

"I have compared thee, O my love, to a company of horses in Pharaoh's Chariots." Cant. 1, 9.

These words addressed to the Bride in Solomon's Song, are constantly applied in the traditional interpretation to Our Blessed Lady, the Spouse of the Holy Ghost. Does it seem a strange comparison? Our Blessed Lady is Regina Pacis, Queen of Peace. Whence this warlike note? It occurs again later in the Song.

"Who is she that looketh fresh as the morning, fair as the moon, clear as the sun, *terrible as an army with banners?*"

In this passage of my text there is, of course, an allusion to the great God in Israel's history, His crossing of the Red Sea, when Pharaoh's host, terrible in its array, threatened with extinction the little company of the Redeemed. But God opened a way for them through the piled up waters, and against the horses and chariots of Pharaoh the chariots of the Lord were ten thousand chariots, even thousands of thousands.

---

* This crown was presented in 1929 by the congregation of S. Paul's, Oxford, one of the early parishes to make the pilgrimage. From that time the image of our Lady of Walsingham has normally been crowned and robed, which was a common practice in medieval times.

It is to this host over against the host of Pharaoh that, when the passage is rightly understood, Our Lady is compared. The note of warfare is insistent in Holy Scripture and in the teaching of the Church. The Church is militant here on earth. For she is the Church of God. And God has an Enemy, who is also the Enemy of Man.

The most ancient of all prophecies proclaims the defeat of this Enemy by "the seed of the Woman." The Woman is Mary, the Second Eve. Between her and Satan, between her Son and Satan, between her children, the seed of the Woman which keep the Commandments of God and have the testimony of Jesus Christ, and Satan there is war to the end of time. Therefore is she prefigured not only by Eve, the Mother of all living, by the precious figure of Sarah, the Mother of the Son of Promise, by the valiant and virtuous woman of Proverbs, by pleading Esther reaching out to touch the Royal Sceptre: She has also as prototypes Deborah leading the hosts of Israel to victory, Jael triumphant over Sisera, Judith with the severed head of Holofernes in her hand.

And the Church today greets Her not only as Mother and Queen of the faithful, but also as overcoming heresy and evil.

Tu sola interemista cunctas haereses. Thou alone hast overcome all heresies. Tu sola; Thou alone. For Mary is the sole human agent in the mystery of the Incarnation of the Son of God. And it is against the truth of the Incarnation that all heresy is broken, as a wave dashed into spume against a rock. The nail that pierced the temples of the anti-typal Sisera was forged in the Holy House of Nazareth when Mary uttered "Be it unto me according to thy Word".

And over and over again in the history of the Church when the power of the Enemy has threatened to overwhelm the Christian civilization, victory has been connected with Mary and out of the Christian victory has sprung a new devotion to her.

It was so when the Albigensian heresy threatened Christian life and morals. S. Dominic fought it with the Rosary. It was so when the tide of Mohammedanism threatened to overflow Christian Europe: its defeat or defiance was a Christian victory claiming Mary as its protagonist, the Deborah leading the armies of the Lord to battle. So it has been, and so it will be to the end. Sola interemista cunctas haereses.

Isaiah prophesied:

"When the Enemy shall come in like a flood, the Spirit of the Lord shall lift up a banner against him."

"When the Enemy shall come in like a flood."

Are we not now at such a time? On all sides attacks are being made on the traditional Christian doctrine and morals. The Christian House dependent upon a true estimate of Holy Matrimony, of Holy Purity, is threatened; divorce is championed, a new morality is preached in place of the old. And too often the Anglican trumpet gives an uncertain note, or even seems to sound on behalf of the Enemy. We learn to our sorrow that our Bishops cannot be depended upon to defend Christian doctrine or even Christian morals. But we must not lose heart on this account. Put not your trust in princes, not even in princes Ecclesiastical. The Enemy is coming in like a flood. But surely here in Walsingham, with the re-erection of England's Nazareth, with its shrine to the Incarnation, the Spirit of the Lord is lifting up a banner. Faith will rally in England those whose hearts are His round this banner. And where there is faith in the Holy Incarnation, faith in the Word made Flesh of Mary's flesh, there victory is assured. This is the victory that overcometh the world, even our faith.

The Shrine Bells

They were cast by Messrs. Gillett and Johnston Ltd., of Croydon.

There are nine at present. They were Baptized by Bishop O'Rorke in 1931. Below we give the list and their names. Some day we hope, by gradually adding to these we have at present, to possess a really fine carillon and a great bell which will boom out over the countryside and be heard by the fishermen on the sea off Wells. At present they are heard ringing at Wighton, Snoring and Houghton, and it is now quite the custom for people to mark the time by them and the Morning Angelus acts as an alarm for many in Walsingham.

No. 1. S. Patrick, O.P.N.* Derrick gave me. In memory, Ann Ayres. R.I.P. MCMXXXI.

No. 2. S. Hugh of Lincoln, O.P.N. MCMXXXI.

No. 3. S. Francis of Assisi, O.P.N. "Praise and bless ye my Lord, and give Him thanks." MCMXXXI.

No. 4. S. Peter, O.P.N. "Rejoice!" William Leeke, Priest, R.I.P.

No. 5. Ave Maria, Gratia Plena, O.P.N., et Veronica S.S.P. R.I.P. MCMXXXI. (This is the bell on which the Angelus is rung.)

No. 6. S. Benedictus, A.C., O.P.N. MCMXXXI.

No. 7. S. Alban, O.P.N.

No. 8. S. Andrew, O.P.N. In memory, Alfred Patten, R.I.P. XV. V. MCMXVII.

No. 9. S. George of England. Pray for Reunion. Constance Ritchie gave me. 1931.

* Ora Pro Nobis — Pray for us

The Extension of the Shrine 1938

The number of pilgrims and the distance of the Parish Church from the Shrine necessitated the building of the Pilgrimage Church. Father Stephenson claimed that the inspiration for the fifteen altars dedicated to the mysteries of the Rosary came from the Rosary Church at Lourdes.

It was on Whit Monday, June 6th, 1938, the fabric being completed, that the extensions were solemnly blessed. Once again Bishop O'Rorke performed the ceremony, assisted by some thousands of pilgrims from all over England. The function commenced on Sunday the 5th, when the Parish Church was packed with parishioners and visitors. Bishop O'Rorke presided, and preached a wonderful sermon to the spellbound congregation. Later in the day he consecrated the stones for the altars, anointing them and enclosing the relics. At Evensong, Father Alban Baverstock preached, and during the office a procession of Orthodox came up the nave and entered the sanctuary, led by Archbishop Nestor, Archimandrite Nicholas Gibbs, Father Polski, and others. Benediction followed. The next morning, by half past eleven the streets were thronged with pilgrims making their way to the Parish Church to take their place in the procession. This was divided into sections. First came the Scouts; then long rows of dark-habited nuns and other Religious with the Lord Abbot of Nashdom; white-robed children; a group of over one hundred and fifty Priest Associates of the Holy House; next, the group of Eastern Orthodox priests, Archimandrites and Archbishop Nestor; then came the Guardians of the Shrine in their blue and scarlet mantles, headed by the beadle; and Bishop O'Rorke with his ministers; finally over four thousand pilgrims. The whole village was decorated with

37

Work on the extension to Pilgrimage Church, looking East.

flags, flowers and bunting. When the Bishop had reached the Shrine he sprinkled it, without and within, with holy water and blessed it, and after the altars were vested, he presided at the Mass. To accommodate the assembled crowds a High Mass was also sung at the same time at the Hickleton altar pavilion in the grounds. During the afternoon the Archbishop Nestor with the other Orthodox sang a Solemn Te Deum in the Holy House in honour of Our Lady. Father Biggart C.R. delivered an oration during the afternoon.

The next morning Archbishop Nestor, assisted by the Archimandrites Nicholas and Nathaniel and others, sang the Holy Orthodox Liturgy at the High Altar in the presence of the Bishop, the Prince Vladimir Galitzine acting as lector and administering the lavabo to His Grace.

In Honour of our Lady

A sermon preached in the pilgrim church, Walsingham, on Whit Monday, 6 June 1938 by the Rev. Frank Biggart, C.R.

My Lord Archbishop, Right Reverend and Reverend Fathers, Brethren of the Laity. You will agree that this, our Day of Thanksgiving, has a significance of wider range than that which derives from the actual enlargement and enrichment of this Shrine, here in Norfolk, of our Lady of Walsingham. It is that wider significance that I would ask you to consider at this time.

If therefore little is said about the history of this holy place, of its glories in ancient days, of its later destruction, or of its completion in this the four hundredth anniversary of its spoliation—if little is said, it is not because we would, or could, keep silent in regard to such matters, but rather because our thanksgivings are most fittingly made, as we have made them, before the altar of God; and because we fear lest it should seem that any who have had the privilege of sharing in this restoration should be thought boastful in spirit, seeming to ask that men should look on them as though by their own power this wonder had been wrought. For as we contemplate that which our eyes can see and reflect on those hidden things which are infinitely greater, we cannot but exclaim, in the words of the psalmist: "This is the Lord's doing, and it is marvellous in our eyes"; and again, "The Lord hath done great things for us already, whereof we rejoice . . . our captivity has turned as the rivers in the south." In the wilderness have waters broken forth and streams in the desert.

I.

Let us try then to set forth in plain words what is the true significance of this joyful day. For its observance will not pass unnoticed, either by those who hold in veneration the Mother of the Incarnate Lord, or by those—and they are many—in whose minds the expression of Catholic devotion to our Lady causes distress; and by not a few in whom it arouses active opposition. In regard to these last, we can but pray that there may come to them a change of heart, since by argument alone but little is likely to be done. But for those distressed and perplexed who are seeking to serve God in all good faith, but who, for a variety of reasons, are fearful lest devotion to Mary should derogate from the honour due to God alone—for these we can do much by careful and charitable words, and by giving the adversary no cause to blaspheme. We must therefore, at the outset, most carefully affirm what every Catholic knows, that the difference between the Creator and His creatures is infinite; and Mary is among the creatures. She is the hand-maid of the Lord; and with us she rejoices in God her saviour.

But having once established that point, we are then free to extol her honour; to sing her praises; to proclaim her distinction; and to demand for her the recognition of that unique place which is hers in the plan and purpose of Almighty God for the redemption of the world. Caution is a word, as we are well aware, which may easily savour of timidity, but it need not be so if by it we mean the striving to be void of offence. We must be careful that nowhere do we ever lend colour to the suspicion that any honour is being paid to our Lady which should be paid to God alone, though we may remember, at the same time, that it is not always fair to arraign at the bar of dogma the language of devotion; nor can every poem be translated into prose. Yet, none the less, we must give good heed to our words. We know full well that exaggerated words have been spoken and written at various times; words which seem, for example, to contrast the mercy of Mary with what is thought to be the pitiless severity of the Judge of all men. And there have been, and, I suppose, there will be, superstitious and unedifying stories to illustrate the tenderness of Mary's love. You may remember that Dr. Pusey referred to statements of this kind in his famous *Eirenicon*, and notably, he said that it had been affirmed "that the mercy of Mary is infinite—that it is safer to seek her than to seek her Son—that Mary is the only refuge of those with whom God is angry." Of such statements, Newman said: "They seem to me like a bad dream, they do but scare and confuse me; I consider them calculated to prejudice everyone, to frighten the unlearned, to unsettle consciences, to provoke blasphemy, to risk the loss of souls."

But why name these things on such a day as this? For one reason only; namely, that we whose delight it is to promote the honour of our Blessed Lady need to make quite plain the ground on which her honour is established.

Mary is unique, for three reasons: first, because she alone is chosen to be the mother of God Incarnate, therefore she is, in the words of the great Easter hymn,

Higher than the cherubim,

More glorious than the seraphim.

since she is the bearer of the Eternal Word. This, which is her peculiar splendour, shines forth with its intrinsic glory when we compare it with all other vocations to which God has, in any and every age, called His elect servants. Mary is unique in her vocation.

Secondly, our Lady is unique in her response to this signal call. The rest of us falter and fail. We accept and we refuse and we accept again. We vacillate and are half-hearted. We are of little faith, and we fear. But from the beginning to the end, in the Holy Mother we find no hesitation, no wavering, no looking-back. Her immediate acceptance is echoed in one of those few words she spoke to the world, "Whatsover He saith unto you, do it."

And thirdly, Mary is unique in her endowments, in what we may call her equipment for this high place. For just as it is true that God suffers no one to be tempted, to be tried, above that which he is able, so also it is true that God asks of no one to perform that for which He does not supply the grace. So it was said by the angel at the Annunciation, "Hail thou that art highly favoured"—*Gratia plena*, full of grace. It is surely not for us to limit the extent of that grace, of that divine endowment. Indeed, in insisting on this, we do but emphasize that all the graciousness of Mary comes from God, even as the splendour of the moon is that of the sun which shines upon it, whose brilliance it reflects, and that all the glories of Mary are for the sake of her Son. Among these glories is the sinlessness of the Virgin Mother. If some of us believe, with the rest of Western Catholicism, in her Immaculate Conception—though the Orthodox are not agreed upon that definition—yet, and here I speak for myself alone, since the formularies of the Church of England make no pronouncement on the doctrine, I cannot hold that we have the right to teach that doctrine as part of the deposit of the Faith which all must accept.

None the less, we must hold and teach with the authority of united Christendom the doctrine of our Lady's sinlessness; that doctrine is summed up in the memorable words of Bishop Pearson: "We believe the Mother of our Lord to have been, not only before and after His Nativity, but also and forever the sinless immaculate and Blessed Virgin. If Elisabeth cried out, 'Blessed art thou among women' when Christ was but newly conceived, what expression of honour can we think sufficient now that Christ is in heaven and that Mother with Him? We cannot have too reverent a regard unto the Mother of our Lord so long as we give her not that worship which is due unto the Lord Himself."

II.

We are thinking of that wider significance which is attached to these celebrations today. I have mentioned the first, which is to further the true honour due to the Blessed Mother of God; and hereby we make also an act of reparation for past neglect, and, indeed, for no small dishonour towards her whom God has honoured so highly.

It is not only that her images have been broken and her shrines laid waste, but it is that her name has been practically forgotten in the sense that Christian reverence and love demand. And we mean by Christian reverence and love the attitude and expression of Christians who hold by the Faith of the undivided Church. Previous to the Reformation there was no difference between the English and the other Western Churches, nor any fundamental distinction between East and West in this matter.

But widely we have fallen away. In England, in former days in the great cathedrals and in simple village churches, you would ordinarily have found two images of our Lady; you would have seen by the side of the cross on the great rood the figure of the *Mater Dolorosa*, the Mother of Sorrows, standing by her crucified Lord. By her presence there she proclaims that the strange Man on the Cross, Whom we worship as God, is most truly man. Elsewhere, you would have seen her image, crowned and glorious, holding in immaculate hands the divine Child, her crown and the glory proclaiming that He is most truly God. Thus true devotion to Mary provides a safeguard of the Catholic doctrine of the Incarnation. Can it be said that the removal of her image and the forsaking of all devotion to her has made that doctrine to be more securely held? Is it not rather true that where the gracious image of Mary has been withdrawn the true nature of her Son has been imperilled, and today is being widely denied? But I speak to the converted. Yet we may not rest in the security of our faith as though it were some treasure to be kept like jewels in a strong room for fear of thieves, only to be seen on rare occasions when safety is assured. Rather is it to be used, and we use it by our active defence of the Faith once delivered. And to that end we have need to be furnished with bright weapons, both of mind and spirit; and to that end we must seek to live within the grace of our salvation, and, therefore, as we need each other's prayers, so most urgently do we need the intercession of the Mother of Jesus, whose children we are, children by nature disobedient, made obedient by grace. For we are the children of Mary, her sons and daughters whose obedience has ever been set over against the disobedience of Eve.

Much could be said beyond the few words that have been said: much indeed, of Mary as the guardian for the future, as she has ever been in the past of the divine humanity of her Son; of the protection which her influence spreads over the Christian home and the marriage state; of the excellence and fragrance of her purity; of the example of her fortitude in sorrow; of her nearness to the Cross—none nearer and no less of her sharing in the divine victory over sin and death, and consequently of her glory in the heavenly state.

It is hard to speak of these high and holy things in words which shall not hide the very beauty they would reveal. Suffer me, then, again to draw from the writings of John Henry Newman, who ever made the qualities of an acute mind the servants of his ardent faith, and gave both to the world with an ineluctable charm.

"Such art thou, Holy Mother, in the creed and the worship of the Church, the defence of many truths, the grace and smiling light of every devotion. In thee, O Mary, is fulfilled, as we can bear it, an original purpose of the Most High. He once had meant to come on earth in heavenly glory; but we sinned, and then He could not safely visit us, except with a shrouded radiance and a bedimmed majesty: for He was God. So He came Himself in weakness, not in power; and He sent thee a creature in His stead, with a creature's comeliness and lustre suited to our state. And now thy very face and form, dear Mother, speak to us of the Eternal: not like earthly beauty, dangerous to look upon, but like the morning star, which is thy emblem, bright and musical, breathing purity, telling of heaven, and infusing peace. O harbinger of day! O hope of the pilgrim! Lead us as thou hast led, in the dark night, across the bleak wilderness, guide us on to our Lord Jesus, guide us home." *Ora pro nobis peccatoribus, Nunc et in hora mortis nostrae.*

Romilly Bernard Craze

K.S.G. F.R.I.B.A. 1892–1974

Bernard Craze was in partnership with Sir William Milner, one of the original Guardians of the Shrine. When the Church was opened in 1938 a man with a stick and a limp was pointed out to me as "Craze the architect" but it so turned out that it was not till after Father Patten's death, when we were discussing alterations to the building, that I actually met him. I knew him to be a kind, sympathetic and humble person who for fifty years dedicated himself to designing church schools as well as churches. He was honoured by Roman Catholics as well as Anglicans but it is for others to extol his work outside Walsingham: our concern is with what he achieved at the Shrine.

In the early days he conceived a great admiration for Father Patten. Because of this he was prepared to put up with endless interference and alteration of plans as the work proceeded. He shewed me many designs in his office with which he had satisfied Father Patten's dreams for the future. None of them ever came to fruition and I doubt if any charge was ever made for them. Such was Bernard's kindness. Subsequently the North Cloister was completed as Father Patten's memorial. Later on the Guardians were concerned with providing more bedrooms in the Hospice as well as a new Refectory. Bernard designed them and produced complete drawings. The scheme was dropped but he took no offence whatever and his charges were entirely nominal. Finally, of course, came the completion of the Shrine Church by the addition of the Jubilee (south) Cloister. To mark the occasion the Guardians gave him a dinner in the House of Lords and a plaque was hung in the north cloister.

The Shrine Church was one of his favourite works. Now it is his greatest memorial—a monument to a loving and saintly person to whom all who visit Walsingham's holy place will be grateful. May light perpetually shine upon him.

Sir John Best-Shaw

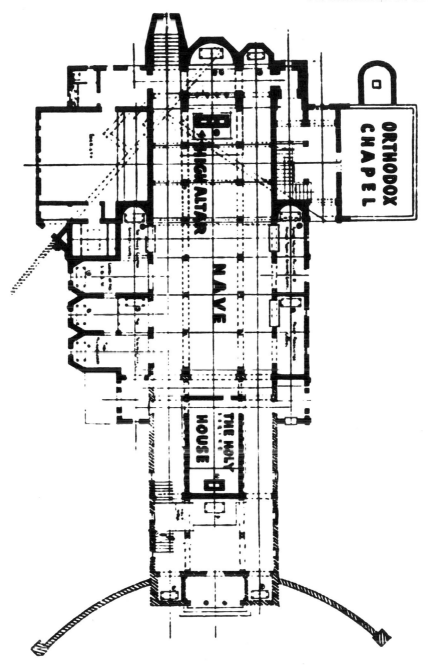

Plan of Pilgrimage Church.

The Stones of the High Altar

When the Holy House was built in 1931, the altar in it was constructed of stones 'chiefly from the ruined Priory of our Lady of Walsingham,' together with a few from other English religious houses. Father Hope Patten evidently continued to collect such relics, not only from England but from holy places abroad.

Some of these were incorporated into the walls of the Holy House, those from Augustinian houses in the south wall, and those from Benedictine in the north. Others were built into the altar of the chantry of Edward I, dedicated on 4 September 1936. The rest were used in the construction of the High Altar of the Pilgrimage Church.

The columns behind the altar came from a more secular source, the demolished News Chronicle building in Fleet Street.

Front.—1. Winchester Cath.; 2. Durham Cath.; 3. Oxford Cath.; 4. Salisbury Cath.; 5. Exeter Cath.; 6. Ripon Cath.; 7. Carlisle Cath.; 8. Davington P.; 9. Dunblane; 10. Hales; 11. St. Asaph Cath.; 12. S. Leonard, York; 13. Whithorn P.; 14. Boxgrove; 15. York Minster; 16. Canterbury Cath.; 17. Ely Cath.; 18. Bulverhythe; 19. S. Mary's York, A.; 20. Elgin; 21. Hereford Cath.; 22. Worcester Cath; 23. Bristol Cath. 24. Dorchester A.; 25. Leiston; 26. Pershore A.; 27. Fountains A.; 28. Zanzibar Cath.; 29. Iona; 30. S. Alban's Cath.; 31. Dornoch; 32. Chichester Cath.; 33. S. Non's P.; 34. Pluscarden P., 35. S. Oran's Iona; 36. Glastonbury A.; 37. Melrose A.; 38. Thurso; 39. Lindisfarne; 40. Llanthony A.

Back.—1. Beverley Minster; 2. Shap A.; 3. Walsingham P.; 4. S. Oran's; 5. S. Columba's Cave; 6. Haverholme P.; 7. Iona; 8. Cleeve A.; 9. Caerleon; 10. S. Duthac, Tain; 11. Bromfield A.; 12. Mount Grace P.; 13. St. Ninian's Cave; 14. Cowley S.S.J.E.; 15. Lynn Friary; 16. Abingdon A.; 17. Maxstoke P.; 18. Finchale P.; 19. S. Oran's; 20. Bodmin; 21. Boxley A.; 22. Tresco; 23. Binham; 24. S. Paul's, Malta; 25. Bourn A.; 26. S. Hilda's P., Whitby; 27. Reading A.; 28. Bury St. Edmunds A.; 29. Mirfield; 30. Hexham A.; 31. Iona A.; 32. Oxney; 33. Wymondham A.; 34. Beaulieu A.; 35. Magdalen College, Oxford; 36. Wells; 37. Easby; 38. E. Grinstead; 39. Tewkesbury A.; 40. Laleham A.; 41. Edgware; 42. Dunkeld.

North End.—1. Carlisle Cath.; 2. Kirkstall A.; 3. Beverley Minster; 4. Dorchester; 5. Bangor Cath.; 6. Godstone A.; 7. Llanthony A.; 8. Walsingham; 9. Cowley S.S.J.E.

South End.—1. Winchester Cath.; 2. Walsingham; 3. Mirfield; 4. Davington; 5. S. Saviour's P., Haggerston; 6. Kelham S.S.M.; 7. Clewer; 8. Tewkesbury A.; 9. Haverholme P.; 10. Leiston A.; 11. Littlehampton; 12. S. Benet's, Holme; 13. Holy Trinity; 14. Edgware

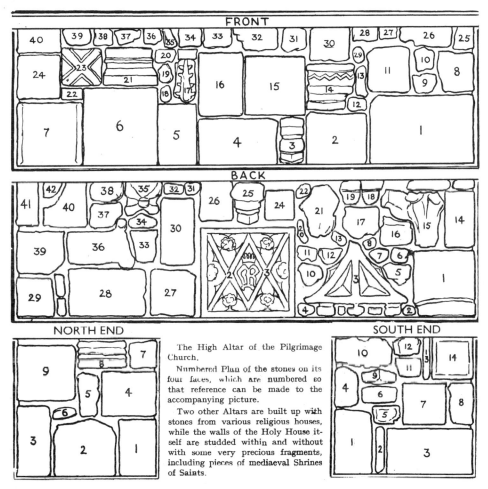

The High Altar of the Pilgrimage Church.

Numbered Plan of the stones on its four faces, which are numbered so that reference can be made to the accompanying picture.

Two other Altars are built up with stones from various religious houses, while the walls of the Holy House itself are studded within and without with some very precious fragments, including pieces of mediaeval Shrines of Saints.

The High Altar of the Pilgrimage Church. The stones on the four faces are numbered, and the key is on the facing page.

The Armorial bearings of Our Lady

Strange! A shield of Arms for the Queen of Peace! How did this come about? The ascription of a "coat of arms" to saints and to Blessed Mary comes down to us from the days of chivalry, the code and ideals and traditions of knighthood. These ideals were high and Christian, enshrined and blessed in the Catholic Church; though, alas! as in the case of all ideals among fallen men they were honoured too often in name only.

The tradition of chivalry was that of honour—in truth, fidelity, honesty and courage; of manners and courtesy; and of Service. "I am among you as he that serveth." And this tradition is that of the English gentleman today.

Service of others was no degradation but rather an honour. Boys of the highest rank were educated as pages in the houses of nobles; and to wear their "livery" and especially that of the King was a mark of honour, as is the "King's uniform" today. This "livery" of service is a distinction of members of the great city companies: the habit of a religious is a livery of service; and the scapular, a part of it signifying holy obedience, in its miniature form, such as that of the Immaculate Conception worn by our own Society of Walsingham, is given as a token of devoted service to the Queen of Heaven.

Chivalry went hand in hand with Holy Church, when Our Blessed Lady was held in highest honour. This devotion to the All Pure Mother of God did so much for the elevation of the status of women and for its gradual evolution to the Christian standard.

The knight was a warrior and bore his shield and helmet with its crest. The distinctive design painted on the shield, by which he was recognised, became the sign of his dignity and honour. He must bear his shield unstained. And so this sign of honour was naturally assigned to saints and to Our Lady, just as we picture her with crown and sceptre of queenship. Among such "Arms" the Red Cross of St. George is familiar to us, as is also the winged and pierced heart on Our Lady's banner, for instance, outside the Shrine.

The Arms of Walsingham

The ancient arms of the Priory of Walsingham, which can be seen in the window of the Lady Chapel in the Parish Church and elsewhere, can almost be looked on as the Arms of Our Lady of Walsingham. The College of Guardians of the Holy House, as a corporate body owning part of the ancient property of the Priory and formed to carry on its work, might claim a sort of moral right to the use of these Arms. But the use

Interior of the Holy House, 1949.

of a Coat of Arms and Crest is limited by strict rules and is under the jurisdiction of the College of Arms, with the authority of the Earl Marshal and the King.

Feeling, therefore, that it would be proper for the Guardians to have the right to their own arms, one of them has provided the necessary fees and obtained a grant of the ancient Priory Arms with a "difference," viz: a representation, in the corner of the shield, of the Holy House. It is a gift in honour of our Benefactress and our Queen.

The Arms of The College of Guardians

In heraldic language the full achievement is: upon a choir mantle azure, lined gules, ensigned on left shoulder with the escutcheon of the college, a shield argent upon a cross sable, five lilies of the first slipped and seeded proper; a canton azure, charged with a Holy House or. Upon a helm mantling of the colours, and crest, issuing from a celestial crown of 12 points and stars, or, three lilies argent seeded or. Motto: Domus Dei: porta caeli. The House of God: the Gate of Heaven.

We may regard these arms as the banner under which we all serve Our Lady of Walsingham. Let us consider them as emblematic of our devotion:-

The silver shield—Our Lady's purity. The black Cross—Her suffering in the dark hour of the Passion. The five lilies—the five joyful mysteries of the Incarnation in her Rosary. The canton of Mary's blue showing the Holy House, the "House of Gold", speaking of the lowliness of the Incarnation. The celestial crown of the crest—the glory of her Crowned Motherhood in heaven, and the three lilies—her purity, lowliness and charity. The motto also speaks of earth and heaven—"Domus Dei," "This," amongst us, "is none other than the House of the God-Child"; "Porta Caeli," "this is the Gate of Heaven," which we indeed find the Holy House to be as we enter the presence of the mystery of the Incarnation in the Blessed Sacrament.

H. J. Fynes-Clinton.

The London Committee for Walsingham

Fr. Fynes-Clinton was really the pioneer in interesting Catholics in London in the Revival at Walsingham and in the 1920's he gathered an informal committee, the main object of which was to raise funds to supplement Fr. Patten's meagre stipend and to enable an assistant priest to be supported. Thus was started the Walsingham Clergy Fund which raised about £200 a year, a large part of this was obtained by an annual Christmas Sale which for many years was organized by Fr. and Mrs. Ivan Whittaker. During the years before the war when the Shrine was being built up this support from London was invaluable.

In June, 1943, when the war had changed the pattern of life in this country, a more formal committee was established, comprising seven or eight well known London priests, such as Fr. De Lara Wilson and Fr. Pilkington. This Committee had as its Chairman Fr. Twisaday, who was then Vicar of All Saints, Notting Hill, and a Guardian of the Shrine. It became known as The London Committee for Walsingham and its main work was the building up of Devotions in the months of May and October, when money was raised by direct giving to the Shrine. A Mass was held in the month of July at some London Church in honour of Our Lady of Walsingham and the Committee directed its attention to propaganda for the Shrine and other activities, most notably the organization of the Priests' Pilgrimage, which relieved the Shrine Office of a great deal of work. From the London Committee, meetings about Walsingham were sponsored at such centres as Brighton. Bournemouth, Birmingham and Southend. So that it changed its name to the Central Committee for Walsingham.

When an Appeal for the Shrine was launched in 1957, shortly before Fr. Patten's death, it was the Central Committee which provided a Sub-Committee to organize this and the formation of the Friends of Walsingham.

Twenty-first anniversary of the opening of Holy House. L to r: *Fr. Fynes Clinton, Lord Norton —, Fr. John Oldland, Fr. Lawrence Harding, and Fr. Walter Hum.*

Walsingham Jubilee 1956

The celebrations commenced with a solemn Mass sung in S. Magnus the Martyr by that constant friend and supporter of the Shrine from the first years of its revival in Walsingham, Father Fynes-Clinton. In the evening of that day, September 20th, a reception was held in the large chamber of Caxton Hall, when between three to four hundred guests assembled. It was a most happy and informal gathering, and the occasion of meeting many old friends.

During the evening the Master of the College of Guardians said a few words about the revival of the devotion and the gradual development of the Shrine itself, concluding by giving a sketch of the proposed programme for the final days of the Jubilee.

Later in the evening Sir William Milner, the restorer of the site to Our Lady upon which the original Holy House is believed to have stood, after giving his impression of the work at Walsingham, presented Father Lingwood with a cheque for about £360 and a copy of the Van Eyck triptych of the Adoration of the Lamb. Father Lingwood, as readers know so well, became Pilgrimage Secretary before he was ordained, and after he returned to Walsingham as Secretary and Bursar, and later on became Assistant Priest. Mr. Patrick Maitland, M.P., made a strong appeal for prayers, asking those present and, through them, all the friends of Walsingham to send him a card, addressed to himself at the House of Commons, saying that the writer will pray daily for priests (and we would add laymen) for the College at the Shrine, which is at present the very great need. We too would add to his petition by issuing an urgent S.O.S. to this, for indeed men are urgently needed humanly speaking to save our Shrine.

A series of pilgrimages large and small have visited the Sanctuary in connection with this twenty-fifth anniversary since September 20th. On October 8th close on sixty priests made a pilgrimage until the 10th, during which, besides their own Masses in the Pilgrimage Church, High Mass was sung and served by members of this pilgrimage. Wednesday, October 10th, High Mass of Requiem was offered for the souls of all departed pilgrims since the restoration of the Holy House in 1931.

In real late summer weather the concluding pilgrimages of the Jubilee came to an end, when large numbers arrived at the Sanctuary on Saturday, the 13th October—the feast of S. Edward the Confessor—some of whom had visited the King's Shrine in Westminster Abbey that morning, while Mass in his honour was sung in Walsingham at his altar. The Pilgrimage Church was beautifully decorated with numerous flowers, the Holy House by our Sister Sacristan and the rest of the building by Father Smith of South Creake, who has such a reputation as a florist; his church at South Creake always being so beautifully arrayed. The choir was illuminated by a number of coloured lights above the stalls and on the screen at the East end, while at night the west front and campanile were very effectively floodlit.

Solemn Vespers was sung at 8.15 that evening, when Father Fynes-Clinton spoke to the assembled pilgrims, most of whom had to sit at his feet (as we all always do) and all over the nave floor. The procession was unable to use the garden owing to the large marquee covering the pathway, so it made the circuit of the Shrine precincts, through the Common Place down Bridewell, Guild and Knight Streets, returning for Solemn Benediction.

Sunday dawned a bright crisp day. After the various low Masses the way of the Cross was followed, and at 10.30 a procession was formed at the Shrine, and singing a variety of popular hymns wended its way to S. Mary's, when at the top of the steps leading into the yard it was met by the Vicar of the parish and his attendant ministers and servers, and entered the glorious old perpendicular church which was

Pilgrims arriving at church steps for Parish Mass, October 14th, 1956.

crowded to overflowing, where they assisted at the parish Mass of Trinity XX, and listened to an oration by Fr. Colin Gill. After lunch the pilgrims queued up for the customary sprinkling while others commenced to offer the intercessions in the Holy House. At 4.30 the departing pilgrims attended Solemn Benediction, during which a few sick were blessed. Shortly after other groups of pilgrims began to arrive, and at 6.30, while Evensong was being said at St. Peter's, one of the three parish churches in the cure, Vespers were again sung solemnly with attendant Deacon and Sub-Deacon when Fr. Harding, vicar of St. Alban's, Birmingham, was the preacher.

At 9 o'clock the palmers (although that is the wrong word, being used properly for those visiting Compostella), manfully set forth into the dark carrying their lights and slowly wended their way through the High Street, all reciting the Rosary. A station was made in the Parish Church, which was most beautiful in its lighting and decoration, where the metrical litany of Our Lady was most enthusiastically sung by the assembled crowd, concluding with a Solemn Magnificat and the General Thanksgiving said for the favours and graces granted by God through the intercession of O.L.W. The route back to the Shrine was by way of the "sunk road." This act of devotion ended with the singing of the Salve in the Pilgrimage Church.

A pilgrimage is not meant to be an easy act of devotion; properly kept it makes great demands on body and soul and is, of course, even when its primary intention may be one of thanksgiving, always part penitential not only in the use of Sacramental Confession, an inseparable part of all catholic pilgrimages, but also in various other penitential acts; the making of the Stations of the Cross, for example, which obviously comes to mind. So it was not surprising that those who had gathered at Walsingham on this auspicious occasion were in church again in their numbers to assist at the offering of the Holy Sacrifice at midnight, and some remained there all the night, while others in groups came to keep watch before the Most Holy. Throughout the night Mass was celebrated in the Holy House by a series of priests. The watch was closed by Solemn Benediction at 8.30 a.m.

During the morning (of Monday) others trod the hallowed precincts from far and near. Again the singing of the Mater Dolorosa was heard while groups wended their way along the way of sorrows, while others drank and were sprinkled with the water from Our Lady's Well. The bells pealed out at periods before the midday Angelus to call all to assist at the High Mass sung by Bishop Vernon, a Fellow of the College of the Guardians of the Holy House. After this time seemed to fly, and before it was realised the Guardians again occupied their stalls in their mantles of blue velvet and scarlet to listen to the wonderful oration delivered by the Lord Abbot of Nashdom, O.S.B., who emphasised so strongly the need there is for greater charity among christians, and prayer for unity so that in God's time, through the powerful intercession of Our Lady and our loyal co-operation, the prayer of Our Lord may be accomplished. May God grant it.

Finally the Administrator of the Shrine, who is also the Master of the College of Guardians, presiding, the last Jubilee procession wound through the village streets circling the precincts and then all standing before the High Altar as with one voice the assembled pilgrims and villagers sang a solemn Te Deum in thanksgiving to God and Our Blessed Lady through whom we had offered our prayers. Then HE blessed us all and with joy in our hearts and renewed intention for the future we wended our way homewards.

Sermon preached by the Abbot of Nashdom
Dom Augustine Morris O.S.B.

On 15 October 1956 for the Shrine's Silver Jubilee.

Luke 1:48. "Behold from henceforth all generations shall call me blessed."

This is our Lady's prophecy concerning herself as preserved for us by St. Luke. It is a prophecy which has in fact been verified generation by generation through the history of the Church. In every age, Christians have acclaimed her as blessed and honoured and venerated her. Yet there has been a variation in this honour and a growth of this veneration as one generation has succeeded another in the long unfolding of the Church's history. Certainly, if we believe in the Holy Spirit's guidance of the Church, we shall not conclude that such variation and growth are wrong; indeed such development has always been characteristic of the life of the Church. Let us very briefly review this development.

If we first look at the pages of the New Testament outside the gospels we shall find only three references to Our Lady. In the first chapter of Acts, St. Luke brings before our eyes the picture of Mary mothering the infant Christian church. "The apostles all with one accord continued steadfastly in prayer with the women, and Mary the mother of Jesus with his brethren." (Acts 1:14). Then we have the brief reference of St. Paul in Galatians, "When the fulness of time came, God sent forth His Son, born of a woman." (Gal. 4:4). Finally we have the reference in the Book of Revelation to the woman who is an ideal figure representing at once both Mary and the Church. "And a great sign was seen in heaven: a woman arrayed with the sun, and the moon under her feet, and upon her head a crown of twelve stars, and she was with child, and she crieth out, travailing in birth, and in pain to be delivered." (Rev. 12:1). Such are the few references to Our Lady in the New Testament outside the Gospels, few but precious.

In the ages succeeding the Apostolic period, reverence for our Blessed Saviour gave rise quite naturally to a reverence for His Mother. This is seen in primitive Christian art dating back to the second century. But it was not until the period of the great councils of the Church that devotion to Mary really surged up like a mighty wave. When the minds of men were so urgently occupied with consideration of the Person of Christ and of the perfection of His human nature as well as of His divinity, it was natural that they should turn also to the mother from whose flesh He took flesh. The Council of Ephesus in 431 vindicated for her the title of Theotokos, "God-bearer," Mother of God. This upsurge of devotion to Mary originated principally in the East, and like many other things in the Church's doctrine and practice, spread from there to the west. Thus many of the more ancient liturgical texts in honour of Mary which are to be found in the Latin office are translations from Greek originals.

Gradually, in the west as in the east, devotion to our dear Lady grew both in popular practice and in the Church's official worship. Then, beginning in the tenth century and swelling in the eleventh and twelfth centuries, there was a fresh upsurging wave of devotion to Mary. In this increase of devotion, our own land played a role, even to some extent a leading role. Its climax was reached in St. Bernard's vehement but exquisitely tender love and veneration for Mary.

It was in this period that the shrine of Walsingham was first founded. There is no need for me to recount again the story of how the lady Richeldis was inspired by a vision of the blessed Mother to make that foundation. Walsingham became a centre of pilgrimage. Generation after generation of our forefathers here fulfilled the prophecy of Our Lady, and upon this spot they called her blessed. It is inspiring to think of the continual outpouring of divine grace bestowed upon thousands and thousands of simple unknown people whose religion drew them to visit this place. Their names have passed from us, the world has utterly forgotten them. But they are with God, and the graces they received from God at Our Lady's intercession have borne fruit in their souls, and abide eternally. The pains for which they here sought relief are long over, the graces for which they here prayed have been granted. All that was good and pure in their devotion abides, stored up in their souls in heaven for all eternity.

Yet we must sorrowfully recognise that there was another side to the picture. We need not dwell long upon it, nor make too much of it. Yet it is a fact that enthusiasm sometimes bred exaggeration and was even nourished by so-called "pious" fraud. It is not surprising that reaction set in: yet it is even more saddening that so much that was healthy and good should have been cut away with what was diseased.

Now we, in our generation, like so many of our forefathers, come to this holy place where the shrine of Mary has been restored, to proclaim her blessed and to receive through her hands the gifts and graces of God. Indeed if we reckon, as is commonly done, three generations to a century, a generation has already passed since her shrine was first restored in the parish church and her statue installed there. We are observing the silver jubilee of this shrine-church, which has seen so many visitors, some devout, some merely curious, in the past twenty-five years. There has already been an upsurging wave of devotion to Mary of which we see around us the material results. But what we must rather look for is the spiritual results for which we must hope, pray and work.

The image of the woman spoken of in the book of the Revelation, the great sign seen in heaven, stands, as I have already said, both for Mary and for the Church. Let us indeed rather say, for Mary as representing the Church. There is in fact a very close relationship between the vocation of Mary and the vocation of the whole of Christ's church and of every member of the Church. This is brought out by St. Augustine in the following passage: "All holy virgins are, with Mary, the mother of Christ, if they do the will of the Father. For Mary also is on this account the Mother of Christ in a way more full of praise and blessing, since he saith: 'Whosoever shall do the will of my Father which is in heaven, he is my brother and sister and mother.' (Matt. 12:50). Mary then, doing the will of God is after the flesh only the mother of Christ but after the spirit she is both his sister and his mother".

"And on this account that one woman is both mother and a virgin, not only in the spirit but also in the flesh. In the spirit indeed she is not the mother of our Head (i.e. she is not the mother of his godhead), but she is clearly the mother of his members, which we are, in that she co-operated by charity that

faithful ones should be born in the Church who are members of the Head. In the flesh, however, she is the mother of the Head himself. Hence Mary alone, both in spirit and in flesh, is a mother and a virgin." (De sancta virginitate, V.5 VI.6).

Mary is the mother of Christ's members because she co-operated by charity that faithful ones should be born in the Church. As, after our Lord's Ascension, we see her mothering the infant Church on earth, so she continues from heaven that same mothering activity. Our own individual vocation resembles hers, for whenever by prayer or sacrifice or by word or example we are used by God as the means of bringing grace to our neighbour, we are mothering Christ in his soul. We are sharing in our own little degree in the sublime vocation of Mary, and we may confidently expect her aid when we do so. This is a precious thought, but I wish to turn to a still larger issue.

When, in some centuries' time, historians come to write the history of Christianity in our day, they will surely see as one of its outstanding characteristics the growing desire for unity and the ending of division and schism. There may be—doubtless there are—merely human elements in this desire, but it is impossible to doubt that there is also a deep movement of the Holy Spirit guiding the hearts and minds of men and leading them to pray and work for unity. He bids us regard our fellow Christians with affectionate sympathy and to try to understand him better, whatever be the difference which separates us, whether he be Methodist or Lutheran, Orthodox or Roman Catholic or what you will. Let me add, the same charity is due, and specially due, to our fellow Anglicans who differ from us. To be bitter against them or to speak of them with ridicule is insufferable. If we strive for this sympathetic understanding, we may often be surprised at the true love of our Lord which we then discover—surprised, and perhaps a little ashamed. We shall love and respect even where truth forbids us to agree; and if others should hurt us, we can take it patiently and try to understand the reasons for their bitterness, rather than bite back.

Now I want to set before you with emphasis the close relationship which exists between devotion to Our Lady and search for the reunion of Christendom. I do not, of course, mean that all who are touched by this desire for unity have a devotion to Our Lady

53

or a full understanding of her position in the scheme of redemption. Yet ancient prejudices do die, and the old virulence against such devotion does disappear. I recently met a young Methodist studying for the ministry. He had had a vivid experience of Our Lady's presence and protection, of which he spoke to his Principal. He met not scorn but sympathy. We shall, I am sure, find that as Protestants regain a firmer grasp on the doctrine of the Incarnation, as many of them are doing, so they will come to a better understanding of Mary's part in God's scheme. Now, if as St. Augustine says, by co-operation in charity Mary is the mother of those who are members of Christ, how great must be her desire to see all who in any degree share that membership brought into one! Is it not characteristic of a good mother of an earthly family that she smooths over differences in the family, reconciles its members and brings all to love? Surely then we may count with the utmost confidence on her powerful prayers for the fulfilment of her Son's petition, "that they may all be one." (John 17.21). What He desires, she desires: where He acts, she aids.

We in our generation, like those before us, call Mary blessed. It is my belief that in our days one form which devotion to her ought to take is prayer for unity among Christians. I believe that Walsingham has a work to do in this respect. To all of you, therefore, who have come here to honour the blessed Mother of God, I appeal to deepen your prayers for her aid in the accomplishment of the divine task of the reunion of Christendom. When with that powerful aid the task is fulfilled, then there will indeed arise a generation which more than ever shall call her blessed.

Victorian Architects and their Successors at Walsingham

Anthony Symondson

THE village of Walsingham has a fundamentally mediaeval character overlaid with eighteenth- and early nineteenth-century facades. In this it is like many East Anglian villages built of flint, timber, wattle and daub, red and yellow brick. It is not a village that many would associate with leading architects of the Victorian and later periods, for I think most would agree that what few modern buildings there are, whether sacred or secular, lack serious architectural significance. Yet Walsingham does contain the work of several major architects even though their contributions are muted and not necessarily representative of the best work.

First among them is Sir Gilbert Scott's pupil, G. E. Street, one of the most influential architects of the second generation of the Gothic Revival. A convinced Catholic, he was churchwarden of All Saints, Margaret Street, the designer of many famous churches, convents, houses, the theological college at Cuddesdon and the Law Courts in the Strand. He was the master of William Morris, Philip Webb, Norman Shaw and the brothers Edmund and John Sedding. In 1861–2, when he was in the full flood of his most inventive period, he restored S Mary's with great sympathy and tact. The Victorians are often accused of ruining mediaeval churches by severe and arrogant restorations which show little respect for the buildings whose life they are prolonging. But the best architects waived their personal style when local conditions justified such a course of action. S Mary's is perpendicular, built in a style that Street at that time would not instinctively have found congenial; yet to those of us who remember the church before the fire it may come as a surprise to discover that the pews, the choir stalls, the canted roof of the chancel and the organ case were by Street. The church seemed so harmonious on its own terms that the only clue might have been the black and orange tiles of the floor.

Of the brothers Sedding, John Dando, the designer of Holy Trinity, Sloane Street, Our Holy Redeemer, Clerkenwell and the House of Charity, Knowle, is the better known. He was, if I may use the term, the arch-priest of the Arts and Crafts Movement, the master of a group of brilliant pupils, of whom Henry Wilson, the designer of the marble ciborium in S Bartholomew's, Brighton was the leader. Like his master, Street, he and his brother Edmund were Catholics; in later life Sedding became churchwarden of S Alban's, Holborn and one of his sons become a Cowley Father. Sir Reginald Blomfield tells us that when they worked in Street's office they helped a pupil who could not articulate clearly by intoning what they had to say in Gregorian chant. They both helped Father Chambers and Dr. Littledale at S Mary's, Crown Street, Soho, a church which in the middle years of the last century was the most advanced in London. A vivid account of its life is given by Mother Kate in her two volumes of reminiscences.

Edmund was, initially, the more gifted of the two, though he is less well known for his early death in 1868. He drew the illustrations for Dr. F. G Lee's edition of the *Directorium Anglicanum* and he had an unequalled gift for designing church embroidery of great freshness and originality. There are some fine examples belonging to S Augustine's, Kilburn. Father Stanton commissioned him to design a white silk chasuble embroidered with the crucifixion and naturalistic flower ornament. He bequeathed it to Father Francis Baverstock, of S Clement's, Notting Dale, and he bequeathed it to the Shrine on his death in 1953. Father Baverstock was Father Patten's vicar at Holy Cross, S Pancras. John Sedding prepared a scheme for the restoration of the church at south Creake but it was not executed. Few architects of that period would have been as suitable for the restoration of one of the most beautiful churches in Norfolk.

The twentieth century provided two architects whose presence at Walsingham will cause little surprise: Sir Ninian Comper and his former assistant, Martin Travers. Travers was a craftsman rather than an architect, best known to a wider world for his stained glass and graphic design. He was the designer chosen by the Society of SS Peter and Paul. His work suffers from the obscurity which falls upon men immediately after their death. In recent times it has excited conflicting emotions. The young (or, shall we say, the more sophisticated among them) regard it with good-humoured sympathy; but those of late middle age (though there are exceptions) maintain such antipathetic reactions that their force suggests a deeper cause than that of architecture. Fashion is more destructive than revolutions and for those who prefer what W. R. Lethaby described as the *ye olde moderne* style, Travers' work will be seen to have few merits. He was responsible for creating a deeply personal version of Anglo-Catholic Congress baroque, much influenced by Spanish colonial models. His best period was between 1911, when he worked with J. D. Sedding's son George, and 1928, when a personal tragedy adversely influenced a burgeoning style. He was a Norfolk man, born in Norwich, and one of his regrets was that he designed so little for his native county. His work is well represented at its best in the restoration of S John, Maddermarket and in the stained glass in S John, Timberhill and All Saints', Norwich. As Architects grow older they are settled with the heady reputation of their youth; it is only rarely that they can sustain their early momentum. That was Travers' misfortune, but one of which he was fully conscious.

In 1947 he was commissioned by Father Eyden to design the small chapel of Our Lady of Sorrows, decorated in his distinctive colours, black and gold rubbed with ochre and varnished. The front of the altar is powdered with conventionalised tear-drops in silver on a black ground. For a time the Shrine possessed some vestments designed by Travers in earlier days for Father Ferrier; they were given away by Canon Stephenson.

Sir Ninian Comper's work is familiar to most pilgrims, not least because of its abundance in villages within driving distance of the Shrine. Great Ryburgh, Wymondham, Mundford and Lound are among the best examples. Comper possessed a rare gift for designing church furniture that has an effortless sense of place fortified by a highly developed aesthetic power. In most cases it is attractive and altogether successful. His work at Walsingham is of his old age.

After serving a pupilage with Bodley and Garner, Comper set up in practice with his future brother-in-law, William Bucknall, in 1889; his reputation as a major church architect was consolidated in 1903 when he designed S Cyprian's, Clarence Gate.

Three windows in the Shrine, of Our Lady, S Thomas and Richeldis, are sensitive examples of Comper's mature work, successful in scale, draughtsmanship and in the juxtaposition of well modulated colour set against white glass. So also is the red silk chasuble embroidered with figures of national saints in gold thread and coloured silks, given by the Guild of Servants of the Sanctuary, at the same time. With the best of Comper's needlework, it was executed by the School of Embroidery, run by the Sisters of Bethany in Lloyd Street, Clerkenwell.

Comper was given the commission for the furniture of the Holy House in 1954, in his ninetieth year. It was finished soon after his death in 1960. Father Patten had long wanted a permanent setting of appropriate splendour for the image of Our Lady of Walsingham. To priests of his generation Comper seemed, of all living architects, the most suitable, despite his great age. In employing him Father Patten was influenced by Father Twisaday and Father Corbould, for whom Comper had lately designed much beautiful furniture for All Saints' Notting Hill, and the church at Carshalton.

The surfaces of burnished gold, relieved by figure subjects executed in clear, Mediterranean colours are typical of Comper's synthesis of gothic and classic motifs, drawn as much from Flanders as from Italy and Spain. But for us, perhaps, the more interesting synthesis comes not so much from old sources as new. The different parts of the altar and reredos are composed of parts of earlier schemes brought into harmony by Comper's great-nephew and last partner, John Bucknall. For example, the shell hoods of the tabernacles are taken from the altar screen at Wymondham; the crucifix and candlesticks (given as a memorial to Father Patten by Mrs Brackley) from one of the altars in the chapel of "All Saints" Convent, London Colney. Most interesting of all, the canopy above the altar, representing the Coronation of Our Lady, is a replica of the canopy formerly in the Stanton chantry in S Alban's, Holborn, destroyed by enemy action during the war. At the time it was thought that the chantry was probably the most magnificent ever erected as a memorial to an unbeneficed priest in the whole of Christendom.

The figures on the rood in S Mary's were designed by Comper in 1900 for the great gilded rood, raised high on a curved beam, set against the East wall of the chapel of the Sisters of Bethany. It was one of the most beautiful ornaments in a chapel conspicuous for the beauty of its furniture, designed by Norman Shaw's pupil, Ernest Newton. The community gave up their London house in 1963. Father Startup acquired the figures, intending them for a rood for S Alban's, Holborn, but he gave them to Walsingham when S Mary's was being rebuilt after the fire. Though they are now almost unrecognisable as Comper's work, their beauty of design and execution maintains a tentative mastery over their present colouring and setting. I hope I shall be forgiven for thinking it redolent of the final phase of Martins Travers' work, though designed many years after his death.

Their presence at Walsingham is appropriate. Comper had from childhood a great love of Our Lady and through his art he did much to promote her honour. The chapel from which they came was the scene of a minor *contretemps* of the Edwardian period which caused wide comment at the time. In 1904 Comper wished to place a crown upon a figure of Our Lady he was designing for the community. The Mother Superior strongly opposed the proposal, saying that it would give too much honour to Our Lady at the expense of her Son. Father Stanton was brought in to arbitrate and his reply was sharp but characteristic: "Tell that stupid Mother," he wrote to the architect, "that an Evangelical clergyman told you that all lovers of Jesus are crowned, including, one assumes, his mother." The figure, one of the best he designed, remains uncrowned in the sisters' present chapel at Boscombe to this day.

1061 is the traditional date of the founding of the Shrine by the Lady Richeldis. The ninth centenary was solemnly observed.

The Conclusion of the Centenary Year, 1961

The Solemn Novena in honour of Our Lady of Walsingham began on October 7th, when there was a High Mass at noon, after which the Novena Candle splendidly decorated was lighted on the altar of the Holy House and was kept burning throughout the Novena, together with nine blue lamps at the feet of Our Lady. Each evening there was a short meditation and solemn Magnificat after Shrine prayers. There was a High Mass every day and when the Priests' Pilgrimage began on October 9th, there were over 70 masses each day in the Shrine.

The Abbot of Nashdom was the leader of the Priests' Pilgrimage, and those who heard him talk on "Prayer" will long remember it as a most inspiring experience. It was a most happy thing that there were many senior priests on the pilgrimage, some of whom have been loyal and devoted supporters of the revival from its very early days, such as Fr. de Lara-Wilson, who has always been ready to place his very great talents at the service of the Shrine. On Saturday, October 14th, there was a good crowd at the High Mass which was sung by Fr. Colin Gill, Registrar to the College of Guardians, and in the afternoon there was a procession presided over by Fr. Pearson, who has done so much on the Central Committee in London, and particularly in the organization of the Priests' Pilgrimage. October 15th is the feast of the Translation of O.L.W., and at midnight there was a High Mass and general communion, after which the Most Holy Sacrament was carried to the Holy House and a vigil kept till dawn. Fr. Gill preached at the Parish Mass at St. Peter's, and in the Shrine there was to have been a Pontifical Orthodox Liturgy at that hour, but Bishop James Virvos waited for almost two hours before the coaches carrying his people from London arrived, as they had been delayed by fog. However, they thronged the Shrine and made up for lost time when they did arrive and after a brief pause for refreshment they were out in the garden singing a Paracletic Canon before piling into their buses for a drive home which, despite the sunshine, promised more fog not far down the road.

At 4.30 there was a procession of the Most Holy Sacrament with four Guardians in their mantles carrying the canopy and Benediction was given at the Altar Pavilion in the garden. At 9 p.m. a procession formed at the Shrine and proceeded through the streets to the ruins of St. Mary's* singing the rosary. Fr. Roe, the Vicar of Walsingham, presided and the processional image of Our Lady was set up in the porch while a solemn Magnificat was sung. As we left the gaunt ruins of this much

---

* St Mary's was gutted by fire on 14 July 1961.

loved church it seemed very appropriate that we should begin the sorrowful mysteries as we came back along the sunk road to the Shrine where a solemn Te Deum was sung. But this was not quite the end of the Centenary Year because on November 4th, after a High Mass at St. Stephen's Gloucester Road, a large crowd gathered at the Albert Hall and heard the Bishop of Exeter from the Chair bid them give thanks for the revival of England's Shrine of Our Lady and introduce the speakers— Fr. Derek Allen, in place of the Bishop of Lewes, Fr. Denis Marsh, S.S.F., Mr. Laurence King and Fr. Colin Stephenson. It was an enthusiastic and impressive rally organized by the Church Union in honour of the Incarnation and it ended by a simple procession of witness which led to the churches of St. Stephen, Gloucester Road and St. Augustine, Queens Gate, and seemed to stretch as far as the eye could see. London is used to demonstrations, but those who took part in this one were glad to be able to witness the simple fact that our Lord was "born of the Virgin Mary" and in their hearts they echoed the couplet which had been quoted from the platform of the Albert Hall:

"Mary of Walsingham, be as thou hast been
Engand's Protectress, our Mother and our Queen."

HOW DREADFUL IS THIS PLACE !

The laying of the Foundation Stone of the Guild Chapel of All Souls by Robert Mortimer, Bishop of Exeter, June 24th, 1965. The chapel, designed by Laurence King, was consecrated by the Bishop of Fond du Lac, October 13th of the same year.

Bishop Mervyn Stockwood blesses the Jubilee (South) Cloister, May 9th 1972. L to r: Stanley Smith, Bishop Stockwood, —, Fr. C. Stephenson, Fr. C. D. Smith. A cloister had been added to the north side of the restored shrine as a memorial to Fr. Hope Patten in 1964.

The Golden Jubilee—15 October 1981

THE actual day of the Jubilee passed quietly as it had been decided to celebrate the event over the following weekend. The Holy House was decorated and the Shrine Church looked very fine with a series of large banners on the pillars made at St. Stephen's House, Oxford. After the drenching of this year's National Pilgrimage, there was a certain apprehension about the weather, but Friday 16th was cold and clear with no hint of rain.

At 8 p.m. several hundred torches were lighted (gold and blue) and the procession made its way through the village carrying Our Lady's statue from the Holy House to St. Mary's. It seemed fitting that for this occasion she should be carried by members of the Chapter, and so the four bearers were, the Abbot of Nashdom, Lords Lauderdale and Gainford and the Administrator. The Vicar of Walsingham, Father John Barnes, greeted the procession on arrival and sang a Mass of welcome with about six hundred people present. There followed an all-night Vigil, during which fifteen of the Guardians led an hour's devotion on the different Mysteries of the Rosary.

On Saturday 17th the Solemn Mass was scheduled for 1 p.m. and all through the morning the village began to fill with cars and coaches, and hundreds had to listen to the ceremonies over loud speakers put up in the churchyard. It is estimated that around fifteen hundred people were crowded in or around St. Mary's for the Jubilee Mass. This was a splendid occasion with choir and orchestra, and was made all the more glorious by the presence of the Bishop of London who presided and preached. After Mass, the statue was carried back to the Holy House to the strains of the

Pilgrim Hymn—she had a bodyguard of sea cadets from Brighton just to make sure that her journey was a safe one! On arrival, the Magnificat was sung in the forecourt before the re-enthronement, and the singing of the Te Deum. Several outbursts of spontaneous applause during the proceedings summed up a sense of excitement and fun which it is hard to sum up on paper.

Later on the Saturday afternoon the local Eastern Orthodox sang their devotions in the Holy House—a moving reminder of the great devotion to Mary in the Churches of the East. At 8 p.m. it was the turn of the Roman Catholic Administrator to preach before Benediction. In a moving address, Father Clive Birch spoke of the debt which all Christians owe to the vision of Father Hope Patten, and of the present opportunities for ecumenism in Walsingham. He presented to Father Colin Gill an address of congratulations from the RC Shrine authorities under the signature of Bishop Alan Clarke (this is now hanging in the Hospice Green Room for all to see).

Sunday 17th saw the celebrations brought to a conclusion with a Concelebrated Mass for all the pilgrims at which Father Colin Gill spoke about the Shrine's development, and of the great gratitude which we ought all to feel to God for the restoration of the pilgrimage. It is fitting that Father Gill should have presided over the Jubilee celebrations as he was present at the Holy House's opening in 1931. All who had the privilege of sharing in the Golden Jubilee went away with Father Gill's injunction in their ears . . . "thank you" for so much achieved, but with so much to look forward to.

A view of the torch light procession as it passed through the village on the way to St. Mary's.

Sermon preached by the Bishop of London

The Sermon preached by the Bishop of London (the Right Reverend and Right Honourable Graham Leonard, DD) at the Golden Jubilee of the Shrine on Saturday, 17 October 1981.

1931, the year in which the Statue of Our Lady was translated from the parish church to the newly-built Holy House, has a number of points in common with this year in which we thank God for the Jubilee of that event. It was, for example, marked by the great slump. There were nearly 3 million unemployed. There was a somewhat desperate preoccupation with domestic affairs and those who sought to draw attention to the clouds on the international scene were unpopular and branded as scaremongers. But it is not to those parallels that I want to draw your attention. It is, rather, to something they have in common which is far deeper and more fundamental, and which the years would not share if we were celebrating a 1500th rather than a 50th anniversary.

1931, as much as 1981, belongs to that era of human history which is dominated by the masculine element in human nature. Both years reflect, to use the striking words of Ronald Higgins in his disturbing book "The Seventh Enemy," "a world of smoke stacks and pylons, pumps and pistons, cannons and missiles; a world ruled by urgency, aggression, appropriation and conscious display." It is not without significance that the nineteen thirties saw the rise of National Socialism in Germany, which was avowedly "a masculine movement", extolling male domination. Today it is to control, power, manipulation, violence that men and women look for answers to their problems—not to love, insight, contemplation and humility. The causes of this situation are difficult to disentangle and assess. It was not so much that the development of science and technology caused it, as an underlying attitude of thought determined the way in which science and technology were used. The causes certainly have their origins in the

man-centred world of the Renaissance and have led to our astonishing advances in understanding the created world of being dominated by a concern for profit and efficiency rather than becoming transformed, in Theodore Roszak's words, "into a sacramental view of nature." The fact remains that, to quote Ronald Higgins again "we must counter the grossly masculine character of modern consciousness and hence of modern society".

It is very understandable that in such a society, women should feel grievously disparaged and under-valued, but we shall not remedy their situation by attempting to treat women as if they were men or by encouraging women to emulate male characteristics. Rather, we must seek to recover the true and right contribution of the feminine to the life of society so that both the masculine and feminine can complement each other in our understanding of human nature and in our approach to human problems.

Modern psychology describes the integrated human being—of either sex—as one who embodies both the masculine element of human nature—the element which seeks to achieve by analysis, control and calculation—and the feminine—the element which seeks to achieve by insight, contemplation, response and intuition. Both elements, though present and signified predominantly in each sex respectively, must find their proper expression in every human being if we are to be truly human. This truth is not a discovery of modern psychology, though it has developed it. It is to be found in the Fathers of the Church, such as St. Gregory of Nyssa in the fourth century and in Dante in the fourteenth century.

But in relation to God, we and the universe are essentially feminine. It is He who creates. It is He who takes the initiative. It is, I believe, a mark of our masculine-dominated society that people can speak of "taking leave of God" or of reshaping the Gospel to suit contemporary thought. But if both the masculine and feminine elements in our nature are to be consecrated and fulfilled, we must first be feminine in our response to Him. Only then can both be redeemed and complement each other. It is this truth which is embodied in the fact that the Second Person of the Blessed Trinity was incarnate as a Man—and is sacramentally represented by a male priest—and that the greatest of created persons is a woman, Mary.

Mary is the archetypal symbol, not merely of the feminine in every human being, but of the response which every human being must make to God. Mary opened herself in obedience to the Holy Spirit to co-operate with God. It was through her feminine response to God that God was able to penetrate our humanity and by His acts of grace restore us to union with Himself in Christ. It is Mary's response which enables us to respond. For her response brought about the Incarnation, in which the Divine initiative of the Father takes concrete form in the Person of Her Son, Christ our Lord. He comes in our human nature and in a human body that we may respond to Him. He comes of His own will in Love to call by love from us our response of love.

But more than that, it is through the feminine response of Mary which enabled us to respond and be united to God in Christ that the masculine element in our human nature can be redeemed and brought to fulfilment. By grace we are then enabled to consecrate and discipline our wills, our minds and all our faculties in the service of God and our neighbours. We are enabled to do so as those who do not possess anything but as those who hold all things, ourselves, our bodies, our possessions, the stuff we use, all as in trust from God, to whom alone they belong. And because that has been made possible by the feminine response of Mary, the contemplative, not Mary the activist who has sought to clutch from God, we are enabled to do so, as the expression of the union with God, into which we have been graciously received, and not in a spirit of seeking to control or manipulate God to serve our ends.

That is first true of Mary. Her generous and whole-hearted surrender of herself in response to God's call led not to a life of ease and comfort. It led to a life of sacrifice—"a sword shall pierce thine own heart also". She was a refugee. She knew the cost in faith and love as she saw Him misunderstood and scorned. She witnessed His sufferings and finally stood at the foot of the Cross. She suffered with her Son that, through His Perfect Sacrifice, she might be glorified with Him. After His Ascension the Apostles, with the women and Mary, the Mother of Jesus, return to the upper room to give themselves to their Ascended Lord, in whom the manhood He took of Mary is glorified, and who, as St. Paul says, will change our lowly body to be like His glorious body.

Response, sacrifice, glory: That is the pattern of Christian discipleship to which Mary calls us.

The history of the last fifty years of Walsingham is indeed remarkable. We thank God today for the vision of Alfred Hope Patten and for his courage and perseverance in the face of difficulties which would have dissuaded many. We pray that he may share in the glory, which through the obedience of Mary, is the destiny of all Christians. We thank God for all who have continued his work, praying especially for the soul of Colin Stephenson who succeeded him as Master. We thank God for the steady increase in the number of those who have come as pilgrims to this Holy Place, many from traditions in which Mary has had little place but who here have found a new understanding of the Incarnation and of the purpose of God for them.

As we look to the future, we recall the many titles which Christians have given to Mary—Ever-virgin, Mother of God, Queen of Saints, Help of Christians, Vessel of Honour, Mother of the Faith, the Second Eve—to mention but a few. Most of these have reflected some need of the church at a particular time, some truth which has been forgotten and needs to be restored, some fresh understanding of the eternal truths of the Gospel. What does she say to us today?

In recent years there has been a recovery—a recovery in varying Christian traditions—of an understanding of Mary as representing the Church in its response to God and, through the Church, humanity itself. In a most striking phrase of Fr. George Maloney, she is the head of the receiving humanity. In the male-dominated and male-orientated world of the West today, it is Mary who reminds us of Her Son's words that if we would enter the Kingdom we must become as little children. It is Mary who reminds us that we cannot use God—we cannot manipulate Him or His Gospel to serve our ends. He does not exist for us. We exist for Him. Mary does not stand before us as the noblest of the human race who has achieved that position by her own efforts. She stands before us as noblest of the human race because she was truly a woman, opening herself to the action of the Holy Spirit that He might fulfil in her the perfect will.

I want to end with some words of George Maloney. "The Church is first Mary, feminine, contemplative, completely surrendered to the over-shadowing of the Holy Spirit. Out of this obedient submission the Church takes on the masculinity of Jesus Christ, who ministered to the poor and the sick, the possessed and the sinful." That I believe is what Mary is calling us to say to the Church today and, through the Church, to the world. May we be found faithful.

The ministry of healing has always been an important part of the Shrine's work. The first specific Pilgrimage for the sick took place in July 1982. It was then decided to build special accommodation for the disabled.

Top, *the site of St. Joseph's Wing was blessed on December 6th, 1984 by Bishop Anselm Genders CR. In the middle of the picture is Mrs. Nancy Thomson who turned the first spade of earth.*

Bottom, *the wing was opened by the Duchess of Kent on October 4th, 1985. The Duchess was met by Canon Michael Whitehead and Stanley Smith.*

Pilgrimage

The same year as the statue of our Lady of Walsingham was set up in the parish church, the League of Our Lady* brought its first pilgrimage—which was a fiasco†— but the village rose to the occasion and the members of the congregation went themselves on pilgrimage, and the whole programme which has ever since been followed was carried out.

The next spring the League brought its second pilgrimage, some forty people coming from London and elsewhere, and since then this Society has brought two parties each year—one in May and the other in the Octave of the Assumption—while other Societies and groups of people have started regular pilgrimages—and the numbers increase each year, so that all the accommodation of the village is taxed to the uttermost.

A pilgrim purchased a property, part of the dependencies of the Priory of O.L.W., which is being used as a Hospice. A second house was also given to the committee. A church and pilgrim shop has been opened. One of the old medals or tokens has been restruck and the clients of Mary once again are to be seen at her shrine: drinking the waters of her well, and walking through the old streets trodden by so many of our forefathers in the centuries that are past.

* The League of Our Lady was founded in 1904, with Lord Halifax as its President. In 1931 it amalgamated with the Confraternity of Our Lady to form the Society of Mary.

† See "Fr. Derrick Lingwood remembers" p.7

Pilgrim badge struck in 1937, a copy of a medieval original. The fifteenth century mould was found near St. Mary's in the 1880s and is now in the St. Peter Hungate Museum in Norwich.

1st Autumn.

Pilgrimage to Walsingham.

OCTOBER 24—26. 1922.

October 24th—TUESDAY.

Party leaves Liverpool Street (to be announced).
Arrives Walsingham (to be announced).

(a) **First Visit to Church** to fix intention, 5. Tea at 5.15.

(b) **Solemn Vespers** (League Office) and Sermon at 7. Preacher (to be announced).

(c) **Confessions.** (*It is an essential part of a Catholic Pilgrimage to make a good Confession and receive the Holy Sacrament*).

October 25th—WEDNESDAY.

1. **High Mass** and General Communion at 7.30.

2. **Stations of the Cross** and visit to ancient Slipper Chapel at 10.30.

3. **Visit to site of Renowned Shrine** of Our Lady of Walsingham (unaccompanied) at 3.

4. Sermon, Vespers and Procession at 5.30. Preacher (to be announced).

5. Conversazione to meet Members of the Walsingham Branch of L.O.L. at the Vicarage at 7.30.

October 26th—THURSDAY.

1. Low Mass with music at 7.30.

2. Final visit to Chapel to **fix resolution** (*after Mass*).

Pilgrims leave Walsingham (to be announced).
Arrive Liverpool Street (to be announced).

(Visiting priests are asked to hear Confession, if required, on the evening of October 24th, and to notify early at what hour they will require their altars so that servers can be provided).

NOTICE (to be arranged).

Sleeping accommodation.—Members of the congregation of S. Mary of Walsingham have offered beds to the pilgrims, about 40 can be put up owing to this hospitality, but in many cases this means double beds, or two beds in one room, it would greatly simplify matters if due notice is given, stating if a single or double room will suffice.

After the disaster of the first pilgrimage, great care was taken over the next in May 1923. According to a cutting from an unidentified newspaper in the records, "Over forty people made the devotions, some twenty coming from London, while Bath, York and even Russia were not without their representative." The London party set off from S. Magnus the Martyr, London Bridge. They were joined in Walsingham by a pilgrim who sent a lively and not uncritical account of his experience to the Church Times.

"However difficult and tiresome the journey to Walsingham may be—and the weather is none too propitious either—the kindly Walsingham folk dispel all physical cold by the warmth of their welcome. On Tuesday, after an informal visit to the chapel, the twenty or more pilgrims who arrived by train made an excellent tea at the Black Lion, and afterwards sought out the accommodation provided for them by the good people of the village. With real generosity every room used by the pilgrims was provided free of charge—no small concession, since many of the villagers are poor—and it is a sure proof of the Walsingham people's devotion to their Church and to the Blessed Maid.

"After supper, the pilgrims assembled in the church for Vespers of our Lady. The whole atmosphere was delightfully simple and homely. None of us had the right books, but we muddled through somehow. We sang hymns in honour of Mary and the Blessed Sacrament, we lighted many candles, and we enjoyed ourselves hugely, though a few of the more old-fashioned might have enjoyed themselves even more had more familiar hymns and the old tunes loved since childhood been used.

"Fr. Williams gave an address. He took his text from Malachi iii. 10–12, "Bring the whole tithe to my storehouse." We were told how the Jews in Malachi's time had settled down into a conventional and comfortable sort of religion, into an economy of public worship. When they paid their religious dues they did so with short-weight coin, because, of course, religion must be diluted with common sense. We were

warned, too, of the danger of becoming too comfortable and self-satisfied. We were not there to make reparation only for our forefathers' ravages but for our own shortcomings, and we must make the great surrender and not drift into a state worse than that of the Jews in the time of Malachi. Again, we were told what wonders our Lady could do for us if we prayed to her sufficiently. Then we made our confessions, and slipped out quietly into a muddy road to splash our way back as best we could to our lodgings.

THE LEAGUE OF OUR LADY
Pilgrimage of Reparation to WALSINGHAM
May 22-24 1923
Journey and Accommodation
50/-

"High Mass on Wednesday morning was an example of a real people's Eucharist. It seemed a pity that it should be thought necessary for the officiants to wear an ugly and continental type of vestment, but whatever may have been poor taste in this respect was fully atoned for by the singing. Seldom have we heard village music so good. The

An early pilgrimage, in the 1920s, at the holy wells in the Abbey grounds.

attendance was very large, especially of the village folk, many of whom made their communion with the pilgrims. That was as it should be—a real welcome from the villagers to their guests the pilgrims and a bond of sympathy which none can break. We ended with Bishop Ken's beautiful hymn, "Her virgin eyes saw God incarnate born".

"Stations of the Cross were a fitting prelude to a visit to the "Slipper Chapel," as it is usually called. St. Catherine's Chapel at Houghton-in-le-Dale is about a mile and a half away, and we ploughed our way thither through mire below and drizzling rain above. Strictly speaking, we inverted the order of proceedings, for we should first have gone to the "Slipper Chapel" and taken off our shoes there, proceeding thence barefoot to Walsingham. However, the road is kept quite badly enough by the Norfolk County Council to justify our retention of our boots, and the vicar brought waders with him—the most practical garment for that day. The chapel belongs to brethren of the Italian

Mission, who most generously invited us to enter and asked our alms for the restoration of the building. The Rosary was repeated on the return journey to Walsingham, while our thoughts went back to earlier pilgrims. I could not help thinking of the last pilgrim to tread the way, and found I was not alone in my thoughts. The vicar asked us to remember in our prayers Henry Tudor, who called upon our Lady of Walsingham with his last breath; he, too, in his early years trod the pilgrims' way barefoot to pray for the life of his infant son who one day, he hoped, would be King of England. This man, of whom many think as the despoiler of the Church, was a true patriot, one who loved England, and whose one desire was an heir to succeed him and keep England united, and save her from becoming the mere plunder of the landed classes. But, alas! when we bought sixpenny tickets and entered the shrine of which but one arch is left, and when we saw the tennis lawn—once the site of the shrine—we saw that Henry's hope had been frustrated. The Church's land came into the squire's possession, the landowning peasant became the landless labourer.

"And so we made our meditation. Besides his own petition, each had a special object for which his intercession was asked. The water of the well is surprisingly clean, and each one of us gladly filled a small flask. It was sad to stand and look upon the shrine, now so empty and deserted.

"In the evening we sang Vespers and listened to another address, and then met other members of the League who came in from the neighbourhood. We shall end our pilgrimage tomorrow morning with a Mass of thanksgiving. We are sorry that it is over, for it has been a wonderful experience to many of us, even to some who were perhaps a little out of sympathy with the League and its aims.

The organization of the pilgrimage was admirable, as was also the provision made for our creature comforts. On one occasion only was there the slightest jar, and that was when we were asked to pray for "the conversion of a prelate to the Faith." But doubtless it was kindly meant.

"The pilgrimage movement is one which needs to be encouraged. Nothing but good can come of it. Combined with the retreat movement, it has immense possibilities."

The Centenary of the Oxford Movement

The year 1933 marked the centenary of the Oxford Movement, and was observed with great devotion by English Catholics throughout the country. The Centenary Pilgrimage to Walsingham in July brought 500 pilgrims.

"Some pilgrims came over night, and Father Lester Pinchard gave his first address at Vespers on Tuesday evening. The next morning there was the usual general Communion and the private Masses of the Priests.

". . . On Wednesday, 19th, after breakfast, the Stations of the Cross were made in the Sanctuary Garden, and about 11 o'clock cars and coaches began to arrive for the Pontifical High Mass which was sung in the Parish Church, after which 500 pilgrims, including the Abbot of Nashdom attended by some of his monks, a number of other Religious and 60 priests, went in procession through the village to the Shrine, singing the Rosary. . . After lunch intercessions and the sprinkling of pilgrims followed as usual. At 4.30 the Hickleton Altar Pavilion (given by the late Lord Halifax) was used for the first time at Walsingham for Solemn Benediction." *(Our Lady's Mirror)*.

At the procession of the Blessed Sacrament the Monstrance was carried under a scarlet canopy, borne by four laymen—the Duke of Argyll, Sir John Shaw, Sir William Milner and Capt. Garrett. Scouts from Stepney lined part of the route. Then followed a last visit to the Holy House, and the day pilgrims set out for home.

Part of the crowd during the centenary pilgrimage.

Pilgrim Hymn of our Lady of Walsingham

The Pilgrims' Hymn was written by Sir William Milner. The first issue of Our Lady's Mirror in 1926 mentions its being sung to the Lourdes tune. It was revised by Father Stephenson in 1960.

SING the glories of Mary, celestial-crowned,
All-loving, all-lowly, o'er women renowned.
Ave, Ave, Ave, Maria! Ave, Ave, Ave, Maria!

Chant the story, full wondrous, how Nazareth's Home
For England was builded in Walsingham's combe.
    Ave, &c.

"Twas when Edward Confessor, ruled over our land,
The saintly, the gracious, neath God's high command,
    Ave, &c.

To Richeldis, a matron full blameless in life,
Who sought for the Star that leads safe through our strife.
    Ave, &c.

Our Lady, all-clement, was pleased to appear,
And her voice, sweetly sounding, Richeldis did hear:
    Ave, &c.

"I come now to ask you, dear daughter of mine,
On the lands of your fathers to build me a shrine:
    Ave, &c.

"See build from this model my arms now enfold—
Tis Nazareth's homestead, more precious than gold,
    Ave, &c.

"Where Jesus, my Lord, on my bosom once laid;
Thrice holy the house where His baby feet played.
    Ave, &c.

70

"And this shrine's dedication the honour shall tell
Of that mystical season when came Gabriel,
    Ave, &c.

"To announce unto me that on Christmas's fair morn
Of my womb should the Lord of Redemption be born.
    Ave, &c.

"And the spot that I choose where the House shall arise,
By a sign shall be plainly revealed to your eyes."
    Ave, &c.

Next morn when Richeldis went abroad in the meads
With her chaplain conversing, and saying her bedes,
    Ave, &c.

Lo! springs bright as crystal burst forth from the plain
Where but now the green pastures unbroken had lain.
    Ave, &c.

"The Sign that was promised see, father, revealed!
O God, for Thy goodness our thanks now we yield,"
    Ave, &c.

Thus in joy quoth the matron. Forthwith goodly store
Of oak-trees was hewn, and of rushes galore.
    Ave, &c.

Right soon the good timbers in order were laid,
And the walls, newly rising, stood forth in the glade.
    Ave, &c.

When lo! in the night came a bright angel-band,
And the work was completed by Mary's own hand.
    Ave, &c.

In the morn when the builders to work did proceed,
They found not the chapel, half built, in the mead:
    Ave, &c.

For garnished, completed, from where it had been
Full ten score of paces translated twas seen:
    Ave, &c.

In wonder they stood and in awe at this sight,
As they gazed on the fruits of that wonderful night.
    Ave, &c.

And there, where Our Lady has founded it sure,
The chapel for centuries long did endure.
    Ave, &c.

Came pilgrims in thousands, this wonder to view,
To praise our dear Lady, her help to pursue.
    Ave, &c.

The Canons of Austin its guardians became,
And a glorious Minister their labours did frame:
    Ave, &c.

Then lofty was builded God's altar of grace;
And hard by the Lord's dwelling, His mother had place:
    Ave, &c.

And the shrine was with heavenly radiance dight,
With gold and with gems as the firmament bright:
    Ave, &c.

Here stood the fair image, miraculous styled,
Of Mary, soft cradling her glorious Child.
    Ave, &c.

Here for love of their Mother, their vows for to pay
Came the faithful, nor even went empty away;
    Ave, &c.

Here the sick and the suff'ring, invoking her aid,
At the shrine, in the waters, full often were laid:
    Ave, &c.

And Mary her Son in high Heaven besought,
And many a healing miraculous wrought;
    Ave, &c.

And many the graces and favours bestowed
On those who in faith took the pilgrimage road.
    Ave, &c.

And last came a king and his virtuous queen
To pray that their bed might be blessed with a wean;
    Ave, &c.

Who, alack, on the shrine cast his covetous eyes
And the gold that shone fairer than stars of the skies.
    Ave, &c.

The order went forth: and by impious hands
That shrine was despoiled, and stolen the lands;
    Ave, &c.

But his soul did repent, when he came for to die,
And to Walsingham's Lady for mercy did cry.
    Ave, &c.

Yet though all seemed as ended, the Dark Ages through
Faithful hearts turned to Mary to offer their due:
    Ave, &c.

Though no more stood the shrine so resplendent to see,
A thin stream of pilgrims still sought grammercy.
    Ave, &c.

Till at last, when full measure of penance was poured,
In her home see the honour of Mary restored:
    Ave, &c.

Again neath her image the tapers shine fair,
In her children's endeavours past wrongs to repair.
    Ave, &c.

Again in her home her due honour is taught:
Her name is invoked, her fair graces besought:
    Ave, &c.

And the sick and the maimed seek the pilgrimage way,
And miraculous healing their bodies display.
    Ave, &c.

Oh Mother, give heed to the prayer of our heart,
That your glory from here never more may depart.
    Ave, &c.

Now to God the All-Father, and Son, with due praise,
And Life-giving Spirit, thanksgiving we raise.
    Ave, &c.

The Intention of a Pilgrim

In preparation for our pilgrimage to the Shrine of our Lady of Walsingham we desire to make clear to ourselves our purpose and intention as pilgrims.

The intention of every pilgrimage is surely five-fold.

First of all, we are hoping to have an enjoyable and joyous outing, the pleasures of a journey in pleasant company, and the interest of new scenes and experiences. This is the lowest motive of a pilgrim: but we need not be ashamed to acknowledge it, for though lowest it is not low. Devotion to the Blessed Virgin Mary blends readily with natural human enjoyments. We think of her as pre-eminently the Mother, the Mother of Jesus, and therefore also the Mother of all Christians, the members of Jesus Christ: and we feel sure that whatever is natural and innocent and happy cannot be far from her motherly heart. We remember that she was kindly concerned to promote the jollity of the party at Cana.

But this natural joy should have its root in a spiritual devotion to the Blessed Virgin: for our outing is not to just anywhere, but to a Shrine of St. Mary our Mother. Our intention is to give expression to our Christian faith and love towards the Mother by whom God came in flesh into our world. We wish to do homage to her whom God magnified above all other created beings, and to give our thanks to her who gave us Jesus. And we desire to show this devotion of ours in that manner which has become established and approved throughout the Church Catholic, by making pilgrimage to one of the many places which an appearing of St. Mary has marked out as hers. Other lands have their shrines: the English Shrine has been at Walsingham, ever since St. Mary appeared there in 1061 to the good woman Richeldis. Devotion to St. Mary is not foreign to us; it is genuinely English.

And, thirdly, we wish to make our devout pilgrimage as an act of reparation. We come, not only on our own behalf, but also on behalf of the many who neglect St. Mary, and do not think of her with reverence or love, because they do not believe in the Incarnation of the Son of God, or hold the strange half-belief which makes them think that honour given to the Mother is honour taken away from her Son. St. Mary is the greatest human benefactor of mankind, and by the fervour of our pilgrimage we wish to do what we can to make up for the cold ingratitude of the world towards her.

Fourthly, it is probable that we come intending to ask the benefit of St. Mary's intercession; for we have little power to make good prayers by ourselves. We shall ask her prayers for the reunion of Christendom, for the Church of England with its many needs, for a blessing on the Holy House of Walsingham and all who visit it, and for our home parish: and probably each of us will have some private intention of great importance to us personally.

All who contemplate devoutly the Incarnation of God and the Motherhood of the Blessed Virgin will come sooner or later to realise how strong and prevailing must be the prayers of her who is the closest of all to Jesus, united to Him by the fact of her Motherhood (she is still His Mother, for He still is Man), and by her freedom

73

from all sinfulness. It is the will of the Lord Jesus, who "ever liveth to make intercession for us," that not only His Mother but also all the faithful members of His Church in their several degrees should join with Him in His intercession. And all our prayers and the prayers of the Saints in heaven and the prayers of the Mother of God are made, and can be made, only "through Jesus Christ our Lord" and His all-availing Sacrifice. When we say "Holy Mary, pray for us," we are but asking her to speak to Him of human needs, and we learn gradually by experience how very willing she is to pray for us, and He to hear her prayers.

But there may be some pilgrims to whom St. Mary's intercession is a strange thought. Not everyone who loves St. Mary as the Mother of Jesus has yet passed onward to a clear understanding of her present work as intercessor, or even of the lawfulness of saying. "Holy Mary, pray for us." No one should feel obliged to do at Walsingham anything that seems unnatural or undesirable. We are "planted by the waterside" of truth, and we shall bring forth our fruit "in due season." Meanwhile each takes part in the pilgrimage in whatever way suits his degree of grace and knowledge.

Enjoyment, homage, reparation, petition—all these, if sincere, are united and hallowed by our worship of Jesus Christ, the Son of Mary. This worship is our fifth and chief intention as pilgrims. It is because St. Mary is the Mother of the Saviour that we do her service at Walsingham. We do not know the Mother apart from her Son. A devotion that stopped at Mary would not be Christian. She pointed out her Son to the servants at Cana, and said, "Whatsoever He saith unto you, do it": and we in our turn will find, if our devotion to St. Mary is sound and wholesome, that it leads us to Jesus. Far from forgetting Him, we shall turn to Him more than ever before. And we shall think of Him more correctly and worthily. His true Godhead and His true Manhood: devotion to St. Mary has always been the bulwark of the truth of the Incarnation; those who disregard her are prone to fall into error about Him, either thinking Him divine but not really human, or Man but not truly God. Best of all, we shall become more like to blessed Mary, in her humility and purity, her obedience and her love: and therefore more like to Jesus: for Jesus and Mary were closely alike to each other, in character as in features.

G. D. Carleton.
author of *The King's Highway*

Enid Chadwick was rather sarcastic about the expectations of some pilgrims.

"Fulness to such a burden is
That go on pilgrimage;
Here little, and hereafter bliss
Is best from age to age."

How nice it would be
if, when we went on pilgrimage
to our Lady's Shrine at Walsingham,
there was somewhere really commodious,
commodious and attractive,
where we could stay.

It is unreasonable that the Hospice
is the only place for pilgrims.
It is uncomfortable;
the beds are hard and there are not enough armchairs
(or bathrooms).
The Sisters are very kind,
they do their best,
but they do not provide
amenities for people such as us.
The drainage system is appalling—
non-existent, in fact,
though that is not the fault of the nuns
or even of the Administrator
because there are no main drains in the village;
all the same, we object.
We would willingly pay
seven guineas a week, or even ten,
if better accommodation were forthcoming.

Let us state a few improvements:
a French chef to conjure up
sole bonne femme and caviare,
Oeufs pochés mornés and the rest:
a good-sized lounge well furnished;
a bar; a band to play at dinner
and an entertainer afterwards (in continental style);
loud speakers in every room, lest we should hear
such rustic noises as the rooks
or Gurney's donkey braying when it is going to rain
(or when it is not);
a show-case from Finnigan's in the hall
in order that we may buy souvenirs for our friends
from Walsingham;
a bathroom to every bedroom.

There might also be
a dance hall and a swimming pool attached
for the rising generation.
These comforts ought to suit the larger purse.

What was it a voice whispered in my ear?
"You cannot expect to find at Walsingham
a Dorchester or a Hotel Bristol."

But, my friend,
that is precisely what we do expect
—at least the meanest comforts of our own houses:
the maid to answer when we ring the bell,
the central heating, and the telephone
in every room.
Otherwise
far better to remain at home
by our own firesides
than face that dreadful journey through East Anglia
to find no first-class hotel
when we reach our destination.

Perhaps one day
our wishes will be granted,
but perhaps too we shall forget
we came to Walsingham on pilgrimage

Fantasy

The Government's reforming zeal
Has reached its zenith, many feel;
And having nothing else to do
Has turned to woods and pastures new.
So, no one was the least surprised,
When Walsingham was nationalised.

They're sending from the Ministry
New plans of high efficiency:
To mechanise the chiming bells,
To sterilise the ancient wells.
Whit-Monday's rush they will assuage
By schemes of staggered pilgrimage.

To all who would this path engage,
The Ministry of Pilgrimage,
(Provided that we clearly state,
On Form X 13428,
Our height and weight and churchmanship)
Will grant a permit for the trip.

We like the soldierly, and warm,
Administrator's uniform;
We love to watch his stern routine
By which he keeps its buttons clean.
With bureaucratic zeal, he yearns
For fresh statistical returns.

Three intercessions we may state
On proper forms, in triplicate;
But everyone shall have a share
In Walsingham's all-purpose prayer;
And pay for votive lights and lamps,
With National Insurance stamps.

Most frightful penalties impinge
On all who would the laws infringe;
And stern Erastians exult
To view controls on Mary's cult:
That England's troublous days are past,
And Walsingham is tamed at last!

S. J. Forrest.

" EL PROCESION "

" At the end of the procession came the Guardians of the Shrine in
their colourful mantillas."

*(Description in a Church newspaper of the Whit-Monday
Procession at Walsingham.)*

Being weary Whitsun-Monday
From the labours of the Sunday,
The pilgrimage to Walsingham I couldn't undertake ;
But the journalist's impression,
Of the wonderful procession,
Has assured me that my absence was a definite mistake.
The modern concentration
On a Spanish destination,
Initiates an exodus that never seems to end ;
But Walsingham is striving,
By efficiently contriving
A strong hispanic interest, to counteract the trend.
The mighty panoramas
Of the sombre Guadarramas,
Were visions that the memory too easily forgets :
Not so the vivid story
Of the clergy and their glory,
In elaborate mantillas and percussive castanets.
" Other years ", assert the planners,
" We shall stress the Spanish manners.
By exploiting hispanophily entirely to the full.
With the clergy in sombreros,
All escorted by toreros,
And a picturesque Administrator, riding on a bull."

But, who could be adroiter
Than the opportune exploiter,
Who's improving the amenities with luxury
   hotels ;
For, the multitudes who vanish
To a destination Spanish,
Will arrive at Torre Walsingham, and seek
   the Costa Wells.

S. J. F.

*(From Fr. Forrest's book, "Our Man at
St. Whithit," published by Mowbrays.)*

Those Were The Days

Kathleen Blayney

*Dame of the Order of OLW and for many years Secretary of the cell at
S. Peter and S. Paul Teddington*

TO the dwindling number of people who knew Walsingham in the early pilgrimage
years you have only to mention the lady pilgrims wafting about the village in blue or
white veils, the Laleham Sisters who ran the Hospice (and lived in one corner of it),
the long queues for Confession after the Saturday evening Procession and Benediction, that special smell that greeted you when you entered the Shrine by the heavy
oak door from the garden (compounded of incense and beeswax and an odour of
sanctity!), the oil lamps and candles in the Parish Church, the cawing of rooks and
screaming of peacocks in the Abbey grounds, Miss Martin, the weaver, in her tiny
cottage with her loom and her cat and her dove, the Pilgrims' Refectory with its long
trestle tables covered with red, white and blue checked seersucker, the Hospice
beds with spreads of the same material, the candles and the old-fashioned wash-
stands in the bedrooms, the large enamel jugs standing on the corridor windowsill,
the creaking boards along that corridor, leading to the bathroom and hot water tap,
the stone-flagged entrance hall with the front door that was seldom opened, the
sitting room with its coal fire. . . you have only to mention such details as these to
see the light of recognition in their eyes and a hint of nostalgia for the good old days!

There have been so many changes over the years that I think it can do no harm
to share these memories with the Few and to show the Many who have come later
what it was like to be a Walsingham pilgrim before World War II.

My own memories go back only to 1932—I never saw the shrine in St. Mary's
Church, but when I went on my first parish pilgrimage the Holy House was less than
a year old and its covering Shrine Church was of the same dimensions as the
mediaeval "Novum Opus". (If you stand with your back to the window of the Holy
House, you will see the demarcation line on the floor showing where the 1938
extension began.)

The altars of the Annunciation, St. Edward and St. Hilary were already in their
present positions, so was the feretory of St. Vincent (the veneration of the relic it
contained being a regular feature of the pilgrimage) and so of course were the steps
leading down to the Holy Well.

In the centre of the Shrine garden there is now a square flowerbed, but this was
once a pool, fed by the water of the Well, and this was sometimes used for the
Sprinkling. (I recall Fr. Reggie Kingdon of blessed memory taking off his shoes and
socks to bathe his feet in this pool.)

The layout of the gardens was much as it is today. The Way of the Cross was
already there, but no pavilion altar until after the Anglo-Catholic Congress of 1933
when it was used at Hickleton, Yorkshire, the home of the first Earl of Halifax (also
of blessed memory) who presented it to the Shrine. There was of course no All
Souls Chapel, but on its site stood a wooden hut, used as a sleeping place (arctic in
Spring and Autumn!) for pilgrims and (later) as a chapel for the Sisters. Where the
modern Refectory stands, there was, discreetly hidden by trees and shrubs, a little
cluster of sanitary cubicles—visiting which was known to the more ribald among us
as "making a pilgrimage to St. Elsan! There was also a very primitive provision of
washbasins.

There was no main water supply or drainage system in the village. The Hospice
boasted the one bathroom already mentioned and one W.C. leading out of it. As you
may imagine, there were legends in circulation of a priest emerging from the lava-

Pilgrims in the refectory (now the Pilgrim Hall).

tory to find a lady in the bath—and vice versa. Even without such dramas, the situation was awkward enough and all the water had to be pumped up by hand—this was one of the manifold duties of William Frary, one of the Seven Wonders of Walsingham, who did the garden, acted as a dignified beadle in scarlet gown at all processions and remained a humble, loyal and devout supporter of the Shrine and its Administrator until he died, fittingly enough on the Feast of the Assumption, 1953. The Pieta in the garden near the Pilgrims' Hall is his memorial.

Another of the Seven Wonders was Mother Margaret, SSM, who came from Haggerston to take charge of the Hospice in 1947 and eventually became the first Mother Superior of the new Priory. Thin and frail-looking, with a skin like parchment, she had amazing reserves of energy and enthusiasm, always found time for a little talk with old friends, however busy she might be, had a remarkable gift for finding "little jobs" for visitors willing to help the Sisters by giving lifts and so on, always saw the best in everybody and took an optimistic view of every situation.

The Hospice Mother Margaret took over had none of its present amenities. Until 1956, when the New Wing was completed, the house extended only as far as the present main porch and gateway. Where you now find bedrooms for disabled and invalid pilgrims there was a ramshackle open barn which provided space (with luck) for parking a car or two. The Sisters still had to live in the wing that had been built on at the other end of the house.

Many pilgrims had to be billeted in the village. Those who slept in the Hospice might find themselves in a large double bedroom or in a tiny attic reached by the steep wooden staircase which still leads unobtrusively from the first floor. There was no hot water unless one fetched it from the bathroom. And those beds! The worst ones were in the attics, but there were some iron-framed instruments of torture in the first floor rooms too.

On the ground floor the space now occupied by the larger green reception lounge comprised a sitting room, cosy with an open fire in cold weather, next to it Mother's small office, then the hall (with the existing main staircase leading off it), then the dining room used by visitors who outstayed a weekend pilgrimage. The present red lounge, shrine of Television, was the kitchen, equipped with old-fashioned dresser, scrubbed wooden table and a huge Aga stove. Here was prepared and cooked all the food which had to be carried across to the Refectory (once a barn, now the Pilgrims' Hall). Here there were only hotplates, no stoves, and yet the plates of food handed round by willing helpers were always piping hot.

We sat on chairs and benches at those long tables, chatting to pilgrims from other churches all over the country as well as our own, sometimes the victims of banter from our own clergy seated at the "high table" on the platform. Here notices were given out and Fr. Derrick Lingwood, Assistant Priest of the Parish and Bursar of the Shrine, would brief us on the geography and arrangement of the place (not forgetting St. Elsan), remind us that the Knight's Gate Café would be open for refreshments after the Saturday evening Procession and, in those far from affluent days, make eloquent appeals for money.

As Administrator of the Shrine, Fr. Hope Patten himself would often preside at meals, but addressed the pilgrims less often. At this point, something must be said about this remarkable man, the Restorer of the Shrine, who, nearly twenty years after his death, is already a shadowy figure to many of today's pilgrims.

The only account of his life is to be found in Fr. Colin Stephenson's *Walsingham Way*. Although this is obviously well researched and entertainingly written, it seems to some of us who knew Fr. Patten as pilgrims rather than fellow priests to over-emphasise his eccentricity. Eccentric he undoubtedly was, as all men and women of genius are to some extent, but to the early pilgrims he was a figure of great spirituality and dignity and charm. In his later years he became more remote, but up to the end of the war at least he was accessible to visitors, with whom he would chat freely, displaying a delightful sense of fun and also concern for the individual—in fact the qualities that endeared him so much to the villagers when he first came to the parish.

He was tall, handsome and had great dignity of bearing—not a person you could ever take liberties with. He demanded a strict code of behaviour from pilgrims and would no doubt shudder at some of the things that are tolerated in these free and easy days! A notice in the Hospice hall made it clear that early morning cups of tea before Communion were not allowed; conversation in the Shrine or Shrine garden was frowned upon and no women entered the Shrine with uncovered head.

Nevertheless, he allowed his cat, Nicholas, to pave the way for later feline incursions into the Shrine. There is testimony to this in the portrait of Nicholas which Enid Chadwick incorporated in her murals in St. Joseph's chapel (look for it to the left of the altar). One evening, a friend and I went to say our prayers in the Shrine before bedtime and found an Office being said in choir, with Fr. Patten standing at the lectern and Nicholas at his side. Suddenly the cat crouched as though about to spring on to the lectern, whereupon Fr. Patten turned and with a stately gesture indicated that the cat should be removed. Which he was, promptly and without fuss.

Fr. Derrick Lingwood was, in his own way, no less remarkable a character. Son of the village baker, he developed a vocation to the priesthood and was impeccably trained by Fr. Patten himself. Fr. Stephenson described him as a financial genius and indeed he bore for many years the full burden of the Shrine's precarious finances. Yet he was always friendly and approachable and one remembers with what pride and pleasure he would show the Shrine's treasures and vestments to interested

80

visitors or explain the progress of the Shrine extension while it was in building.

This new church was blessed by Bishop O'Rorke (a staunch friend of the Shrine) on Whit Monday, 1938—a great occasion indeed, described by the *Church Times* (never very sympathetic to Walsingham) as "a holy beano". This was the origin of the National Pilgrimage. For many years the anniversary of the "translation" of the image of Our Lady of Walsingham from St. Mary's to the Holy House (on October 15th, 1931) was also kept and the years 1952 (21st anniversary) and 1956 (silver jubilee) were marked by special celebrations.

But this is taking a leap forward in time. We must recall the war years, when for a time Walsingham was out of bounds to visitors except in the winter months because of the threat of invasion; when at the six o'clock Rosary (now known as Shrine Prayers) all those from the village who were serving in the Forces were prayed for by name; when special wartime devotions (including all fifteen mysteries of the Rosary recited at the altars of the Shrine) were led by Fr. Patten; when in 1940, after the fall of France, rumours were rife of the possibility of German parachutists disguising themselves as priests or nuns: when in 1944 the nightly thunder of RAF bombers overhead told us that Italy was about to be raided again.

There was a Pilgrimage of Thanksgiving for victory in Europe at Whitsun, 1945 and from then Walsingham began to appear on the map. In the early fifties a somewhat garbled account of the Shrine and its works appeared in a popular Sunday newspaper. The article gave the impression that the Holy Well was a kind of wishing well, but it got over the message that this was a place of healing. The result was that the following day a tide of visitors began to flow into the village, pathetic cases many of them, seeking cures for themselves or their relatives and all demanding water from the Well—requests also came by post, so that the supply of bottles soon gave out.

The ecumenical movement was anticipated in the fifties by a historic radio broadcast in which Fr. Patten and the R.C. priest, Fr. Hulme, took part. For some years an Orthodox priest lived in the village and held regular services in the Orthodox Chapel "upstairs" in the Shrine. He drew his congregation largely from exiled Central Europeans who were at that time doing agricultural work in the surrounding countryside. We Anglicans were always welcome at these services and on Whit Monday some of us would attend the Liturgy before our own pilgrimage programme got going. Even before the war, Russian Orthodox clergy and pilgrims had visited the Shrine and my own first encounter with any form of Orthodox worship was on an occasion when they sang a kind of Vespers of Our Lady in the Holy House.

Fr. Hope Patten died at Assumptiontide, 1958, and this was the end of an era. He had given Walsingham an indelible character, but the time had come to open out "England's Nazareth" to a wider public.

An anonymous priest pilgrim recorded his memories in 1966

I was enchanted by the village of Walsingham which seemed so unlike anywhere else I knew in England. The old parish church had a feel about it which I shall never forget. In those days one was thrilled to hear the Angelus ringing from that tower and not on the tin-pot bells of the Shrine Campanile, which had not then been built. When you entered for the Mass early in the morning there was a twittering sound which was the Laleham Sisters saying Prime in the Guild's Chapel by candlelight, for there was no other. How Fr. Patten had left his mark upon that church! All the shrines and altars which he had erected had some story behind them and had an established look as if the Reformation had never happened. On the afternoon of the day on which the church burned I was sitting there sheltering from the rain and a young man was looking round. I could not help wondering whether it was making the same sort of impression upon him as it had done upon me thirty years earlier. By next day the old church with its sweet musty smell and mellowed woodwork had gone for ever.

The Hospice had a charm all of its own and I have imprinted on my mind arriving late one Saturday evening after a tiring journey from the North of England and there was Sister Grace Helen sitting in her office reading her Breviary by the light of a candle. It was a vision of peace which has never left me. Later electric light was put into the passages only, which was very tricky if you had an electric razor, as I had by that time, as you had to unplug and dart back into your room when you heard anyone coming. I remember also that the bathroom had certain perils, having two doors it was possible to imprison someone in the smallest room in the house while one had a bath.

Then there was all that church chat in the dining room which excited me so much. The ladies all had such very advanced views and I thought what bliss it would be when I was ordained to have a congregation composed of them. With other younger visitors I walked to Snoring and Binham and we recited the Rosary there, feeling that we were striking a great blow for the Faith.

On my very first visit dear Miss Doyle-Smythe, who was only a visitor in those days, got hold of me and asked me to distribute some literature when I got home to the Brighton clergy, and some very smart snubs I got for my pains when I did it! Later she came to live in Walsingham and presided over a little shop in the garden where, as she got more infirm in mind, she gave very curious and muddled information to visitors, but she belongs very much to my earliest memories of the Shrine.

Little by little I got to know some of the residents. Mrs. Payne-Jennings I knew in Sussex when she lived at East Preston and it was she who persuaded me to join the Society of Mary at Littlehampton. I was thrilled by her house there and the fact that she had a large statue of Our Lady with a blue lamp in the hall. When I suggested to my parents that we might have the same the idea was not well received by them. She became disenchanted with her local church and moved to Walsingham where she made the house in the Commonplace most attractive and dispensed hospitality with great generosity. She was not really suited to live in a village and I often wonder if, having known her as a boy, I should have been able to manage her any better than poor Fr. Patten did. I am always so happy the last time I saw her, shortly before her sudden death, she was in a far more charitable state of mind about everyone and everything. And then there were the Misses Hastings who were so forbidding until one got to know them. They certainly belied their background and appearance. One might have thought that they would be very Low Church which they were certainly not; and very straight laced, but in fact they had a racy and mordant wit—and what titanic battles used to go on among these good ladies. I remember being made to join a Pilgrims Club which Mrs. Payne-Jennings had started in the Martyrs' House which she had bought, but it soon came to an end in a monumental row the details of which I cannot now remember, although I had them from both sides. Aylwyn Williams kept the Pilgrim Token Shop and had been persuaded by Fr. Patten to buy all manner of romantic things from Belgium and Italy which proved rather unsaleable, but nothing could quench his volatile Celtic personality and I have laughed as loudly in his sitting room over the shop as anywhere in my life, and that is saying something! Miss Chadwick was already painting away, and it is a definite milestone in the history of the Shrine when her designs begin to appear in cards, publications and decoration. She has such a particularly individual style that one can spot her drawing without looking at the signature, and her lettering is superb.

I cannot remember when Mrs. Ferrier first appeared in the Shrine Shop, but she must have been almost its foundress, and must have sold enough rosaries in her time to stretch from Land's End to John O'Groats.

Miss Martin belonged to very early days and I remember going to coffee in her tiny cottage when she turned over photographs of the nineteen twenties with Fr. Paten presiding at the May Revels and performing very outré ceremonies, within a few years of his induction to the parish. Her little cottage is now a ruin on the way to the station, which is in the process of becoming a ruin itself, but we still use vestments and frontals made of the lovely material she wove.

Enid Chadwick recalled further details about Miss Martin, a fellow member of the Crafts Guild.

Miss Martin the Weaver, known to residents and pilgrims alike. She lived in a tiny "condemned" cottage called "The Haven" on the narrowest part of Station road opposite the Black Lion, where she would work with her door open and entice visitors, who had just arrived by train, to come in and see her weaving. For company she had Micky her black cat, on whose back perched a white dove. Her work was good—both her weaving and embroidery, the results of which can be seen in the Shrine, notably a beautiful red High Mass set and a black velvet chasuble bearing the arms of Edward I. She behaved very strangely at times. Once when Fr. Patten annoyed her she took her work into the little chapel which is Station IV, and where William Frary rang the bells which hung in a little wooden structure above.

National Pilgrimage 1959

The first which took place in the Abbey grounds
'Impressions of Two Pilgrims'

Whit Monday dawned grey and cold. Anxious eyes turned skywards. The question we had been asking ourselves for weeks was now urgent—*what will happen if it rains?*

All was ready for the great National Pilgrimage organised by the Church Union to mark the end of its Centenary Year. The Albert Hall Congress altar had been set up under a canvas canopy in the Priory grounds. Two large marquees had been erected in the Shrine garden, stacks of sandwiches had been cut and packed lunches and teas prepared by devoted hands. The image of Our Lady of Walsingham temporarily dethroned from its niche above the splendid new reredos in the Holy House, stood ready to be carried in solemn procession. The Church Union's President, the Hon. Patrick Maitland, M.P., Master of Lauderdale, had kept his all-night Vigil of Pentecost in the Shrine.

About a hundred pilgrims had already spent the weekend in Walsingham and thousands more were expected for the day. Indeed many had already arrived by breakfast-time. Brave souls, they had set off from Lancashire, Yorkshire and other distant places in the small hours of the morning, and the first advertised Mass in the Shrine was at 5 a.m. At seven the altars were thronged, and all through the morning coach after coach discharged its load of blue-badged travellers. Cassocked figures of all shapes and sizes appeared in the Common Place or led their little bands through the mazes of the Via Dolorosa in the Shrine Garden.

The Shrine Shop did a brisk trade in pilgrim badges, rosaries, books, statues, etc., but we suspected that some people lingered for shelter from the keen wind outside! Then out came the sun and the shop was almost empty—for the moment. Our Lady had heard our Prayer. The sky was true Walsingham blue and the sun's

Panoramic view of the National Pilgrimage, 1980.

rays were warm as we streamed through the Priory Gate for 1.15 p.m. High Mass and Procession. A perfect afternoon!

"Now there was much grass in the place" which had once been the vast nave of the Augustinian Priory Church, and here the pilgrims sat down, "in number about five thousand". A B.B.C. recording van stood in the background and some who read this may have heard the broadcast in Radio Newsreel that same evening.

The Mass was sung in the presence of the Bishop of Thetford, representing the Bishop of Norwich, by Fr. Colin Gill and the sermon preached by the Shrine's new Administrator, Fr. Colin Stephenson. Looking up at the great ruined arch behind the altar, one wondered, were the long-dead monks watching with approval this return to their ancient Sanctuary? And was the spirit of Fr. Hope Patten, Restorer of the Shrine, rejoicing at such a splendid witness to the fruitfulness of his own life's work?

Now it was time for the great Procession—rumoured to be two miles long—to wind its way out onto the Sunk Road, past S. Mary's Church, up the High Street and downhill again to the Shrine, singing over and over the pilgrim hymn which tells the story of England's Nazareth. A group of Protestant Alliance demonstrators stood silently holding their futile banners and leaflets as our "Aves" resounded in the narrow street. We had our own banners, however, from parishes far and wide. One, proudly borne by capped and gowned undergraduates, proclaimed: "Oxford at the feet of O.L.W." The tail end of the procession was still singing the hymn when Benediction was given from the porch of the Shrine Church to the pilgrims packed in and around the courtyard.

Then the crowds dispersed for tea and at length the coaches, full of tired but happy pilgrims, rumbled away to face once more the traffic jams, the noise and bustle of towns and cities. And Little Walsingham slept in peace.

The First Official Ecumenical Pilgrimage 12 July 1970

"Official", because there have been many joint pilgrimages before, but they have been limited to particular districts, or to schools. This year's pilgrimage was general: for everybody who could come. It started with Mass, celebrated by the Bishop of Lynn, in the Shrine, and another for Roman Catholics in the Slipper Chapel. In the Shrine, the lesson was read by a priest from Kuching, and an assistant secretary of M.E.C.C.A. was present, so it was missionary as well as ecumenical. After lunch, everyone went to the Slipper Chapel. There was an official welcome from the Bishop of Elmham, then a procession in silence to the Shrine gardens. There, a joint service took place. The Bishop of Lynn in his turn gave an official welcome. A Methodist minister said the prayers, Fr. Noel Godwin, Chaplain of All Hallows School, Ditchingham, preached, and the two Bishops gave a joint blessing.

The First Parliamentary Pilgrimage 1973

On Wednesday, May 16th, over thirty peers, Members of Parliament and their wives and families took part in the first Parliamentary pilgrimage to Walsingham. The pilgrimage was organised by the Earl of Lauderdale and included members of both Houses of Parliament which probably made it the first act of State at Walsingham since Henry VIII's visit in the early 16th century. All denominations were represented and services were held in both Shrines. During the afternoon a procession was made through the streets to the grounds of Walsingham Abbey for an ecumenical service of witness conducted by Bishop Clark, Dr. Stockwood, Father Alan Carefull (Administrator of the Shrine), and the Methodist Minister, the Revd. Edwin Softley. It was a happy and significant day.

The College of Guardians

The College was formed in 1931 although not formally constituted until the following year. The Guardians' distinctive insignia only gradually evolved. The blue mantles were first worn in 1938; their stars were struck in 1947. The Master's silver gilt chain was presented by Father Fynes-Clinton in 1933. Provision for Honorary and Emeritus Guardians was made in 1946.

Father Hope Patten was Master of the College as well as Administrator of the Shrine from the start until his death. Since 1968 the offices have been divided.

In the following pages all the notices about deceased Guardians from the Shrine publications are reprinted. Some are very sketchy and there are no notices of some very distinguished lay Guardians such as the Duke of Argyll and Sir Eric Maclagan, the Director of the Victoria and Albert Museum.

The Shrine is vested in twenty Guardians who also form the Walsingham College Trust Association, a charitable trust company. They act in accordance with the Constitution of the College of Guardians and the Articles of Association of the Trust Company. They are concerned with all aspects of the Shrine's work, they meet in May when the Bursar presents accounts previously approved by the Directors (elected from among the Guardians) and in October. At both meetings the Administrator (appointed by the Guardians for the day-to-day running of the whole work of the Shrine in Walsingham) gives a report on the past six months. A priest Guardian is elected as Master, to be their executive head, and he maintains close relations with the Shrine and is frequently there for consultation with the Administrator and others. Another Guardian is elected as Registrar to act as his deputy at need. Broadly, Guardians are elected by a carefully designed voting system mainly on their particular ability to be of service to the Shrine, partly to represent a particular area, and always on having shown a devotion to the Shrine and its work. In addition, a

The Guardians, 1955: standing l to r Fr. Lester Pinchard, Fr. Twisaday, Fr. Lingwood, Fr. Crusha, Lord Norton, Fr. Wodehouse, Fr. Stephenson, Sir William Milner, Fr. Rayner CR. Master of Lauderdale, Mr. George Long, Sir John Best-Shaw. Seated Fr. Fynes-Clinton, Fr. Hope Patten.

small number of Honorary Guardians are chosen, without voting powers, (including several bishops) as being sympathetic to the Shrine and able to be useful counsellors.

There is a Patronage Committee to deal with the Shrine's ecclesiastical patronage. This meets as required. The Guardians also own Quainton Hall School, Harrow (some Guardians are chosen as Governors) and are trustees for Parcevall Hall Yorkshire (now used as Bradford Diocesan Retreat House). A yearly report is made to the Guardians on them.

John Colin Stephenson, Priest

Master 1958–73
Administrator 1958–68
Vicar of S. Mary Magdalen Oxford 1948–59
died 14 August 1973

It is with joy and gladness that we will always associate Colin Stephenson. Whether you knew him as a speaker at some purely secular function or at your own dinner table: whether you knew him as a priest and confessor: as a member of some clerical gathering, as Administrator of this Shrine and Master of its Guardians: as a preacher or as a personal friend, it was the same quality of exultation, gladness and joy that he conveyed. Personally, I had known him probably longer than most of you here—for 39 years, to be precise. Whether we were walking on Boars Hill, near Oxford, or visiting some country church which was not all our undergraduate minds thought appropriate, at some undergraduate party or listening to some pompous ecclesiastic, his quality of laughter and irrepressible joy in living, even with the foibles and peculiarities of others, was always there, and was never lost all through his life. Indeed, the frustrations seemed at times only to add fuel to the fire and make life seem even more humorous than before. After his disastrous accident in Ceylon, which he described in horribly graphic but still amusing terms, he told of the day when he began to walk again on crutches and was visited by a friend who himself tripped and fell prostrate on the ground. Or, driving in a narrow Norfolk lane (a lane which typically led to Gasché's restaurant,) another car came round a bend and collided with him. The driver proved to be the lady Church-warden of a neighbouring parish. On both these occasions, he told me: "I simply roared with laughter". In Oxford, at St. Mary Magdalen's, where he probably found his greatest fulfilment, it was his joyous presentation of the Catholic religion which attracted so many who remember him gratefully, and at Walsingham, if it had been regarded with more than a little suspicion hitherto, the gladness and joy which be brought commended it to large numbers: for it celebrates one whose spirit rejoiced in God our Saviour.

But laughter and gladness can be superficial and unreal; there is that terrible clerical heartiness and that forced clerical smile which make gentler spirits squirm. To imagine that Colin Stephenson's joy was superficial is to show that you did not know him, and it was his freedom from the inhibitions and artificialities that take the joy out of many lives that commended him. If at times he was theatrical, it was because the theatre was part of his nature! There may be some here who attended his retreats or sought his help in times of spiritual distress, and so were able to draw on the spiritual depths that were behind the flamboyance. Again, laughter can be cynical. Cynicism can be one of the faults of the clergy after a time; it means that a certain bitterness has crept in. There were many things in Colin's life which might have embittered others, and he was not always as insensitive to the lack of consideration by others as he seemed; but there was never any trace of cynicism, even when there was reason for disillusion and disappointment with the clergy, the Church or the world. All had their weaknesses, and over and over again when perhaps the shortcomings of some one or other have been too blatant to avoid, he has said: "But he is terribly good with so and so". Again, laughter can be uncharitable; if you have a ready wit, you can be very unkind and use others to show your own cleverness. Colin was certainly tremendously tolerant, even to a fault, and if he could not always hide his feelings, was greatly hurt if he had been unkind inadvertently to someone who could not answer back.

The fact is that this gladness and joy came from the source Ecclesiasticus alleges: from the fear of the Lord. It is difficult, perhaps impossible, to feel or impart real joy if the mind is not at ease, if in the centre of one's life, in one's home, there is no peace. And Colin was very much at home in the house of God: he felt a sense of familiarity almost with the Mother of the Lord and the Mother of all Christians which sometimes shocked those who did not understand it. The Christian faith is about joy, it is one of the fruits of the spirit, the great cause of all our joy is honoured in this place, and it was the sheer joy in believing that Colin wanted men to share with him. He could not understand dullness in religion, and it was that, certainly in earlier days, which made his religious expression so exuberant. It is only the hesitant, the uncertain, who make of the Christian a hard, a sad and heavy thing. It was the complete absence of dullness which made him so acceptable and so great a friend and counsellor to sailors, among undergraduates and dons in Oxford: in tiny villages and the lovely country houses of Norfolk: among priests and agnostics: in the Shrine of Our Lady of Walsingham and in some respectable parish church or half-fearful public school chapel. Any suspicion that he was over concerned with the trappings of religion (and he himself was partly responsible for this impression in his autobiography) was quickly dispelled. It was the supernatural, the fullness of the faith that people really wanted, because it gave life and made them free; but it must be given to them in ways which made it possible for them to digest it. He was not the victim of slogans and clichés, and this explained the apparent change in his outlook and expression in the last few years. The world was a different world from the 1930's, but it needed the same faith, and confused men and women of the 60's and 70's had a different background, therefore the same truth must be mediated in different ways.

In this place one must speak of his devotion to and work for Walsingham. Although in *Merrily on High* he says that it was I who first directed him here, I can assure this congregation that this was one of those charming inaccuracies which make a good story better! Colin walked here on a pilgrimage from London, led by Father Kenrick (the editor of the English Missal) in 1935, and has told of the great impression Walsingham made on him. At that time devotion to the Blessed Virgin in the Church of England had something unreal and artificial about it—it was regarded as something imported from abroad, and might have sinister implications. Colin's devotion to Mary had nothing unreal or artifical about it: it came quite naturally and was very deep. Leaving behind the Oxford he loved cost him more than most people have ever appreciated, but he took on the very difficult task of succeeding Hope Patten. The foundation of the work at Walsingham had been laid, but there was a possibility that it might come to nothing and be just another of those fantastic schemes with which the history of the Church of England since the Oxford Movement has been littered. That this did not happen is, under God, largely due to the work of Colin Stephenson. The years since 1958 when he came here have been a testing time for any institution, especially an ecclesiastical institution, and during that time Walsingham has come to be greatly loved by thousands, a centre of prayer and the spiritual life, and a place of influence in the whole Church. He came to love Norfolk and its open countryside, its villages with their vast churches, and his love for people gave him a great sympathy for Norfolk men and women. He enjoyed ministering in the village churches where he became a welcome visitor and preacher. The Shrine at Walsingham was becoming known all over England and the world, but on its own home ground it was largely incomprehensible. Colin bridged the gap and made it part of Norfolk life, and when he was made an honorary canon of Norwich by Bishop Fleming, it was an honour well deserved and welcomed on all sides. Certainly his connection with Norwich Cathedral was something he prized, and he took a great delight in visiting it and a great interest in its affairs.

It is almost precisely five years since Colin resigned from being Administrator of the Shrine. He was feeling the demands too great and his health had clearly collapsed, but he had crowded a good deal into those five years, and his influence was probably at its peak, for he travelled (clearly, too much) and spoke and preached and conducted retreats all over the country, as well as writing the books which have given much delight and amusement to many, even if others have at times been scandalised. He enjoyed the freedom, but when, last year, it seemed right to both of us that I should go to Oxford, he said, "If you go to Oxford I can come and carry on here for the time being". So once more he took up the duties of Administrator and lived here for five months. 58 years is a short life. When St. Vincent de Paul was dying in a ripe old age he said, "There is so much to be done, so much to be done", and like St. Vincent, Colin had not lost the zest for living and doing, and had so much to give that the world of the 70's needs, perhaps, more than ever. But with him who fears the Lord it will go well at the end and in the day of his death he will be blessed.

It was the Feast of the Assumption, which speaks to the believer of the completion of Christ's work in those he has redeemed.

Charles Smith

Arthur John Colin Burke Gill, Priest

Master 1973–82
Rector of S. Magnus the Martyr,
London Bridge 1960–83
died 20 July 1983

In Father Patten's day Guardians' Chapters were wholly unpredictable, except in one respect. Father Patten's gifts did not include those of chairmanship but they did include those of making sure that no matter what had been decided, *his* decision was final. So motions would be proposed, and amendments possibly carried, but if either were not to the Master's taste, they were simply reversed or recorded in the opposite sense.

Such was the atmosphere in which this writer first recalls Father Colin Gill's contributions. There was never lacking, however unpredictable the course of a Guardians' meeting, a merry undercurrent of mirth and of surprise. Often seated beside the ebullient Colin Stephenson, and near a mildly disapproving Father Raymond Raynes C.R., Father Colin always seemed preoccupied with keeping an irrepressible sense of humour under control. Here is a characteristic which marked every one of his activities, even the most solemn. The absurd side of things is never far away.

No doubt his discipline in humour control had been developed over the years. For Father Colin Gill is one of the old Guard. He had known Father Patten for many years before he became a Guardian in 1953. He was Registrar from 1958 to 1973 and Master from 1973 to 1982.

It is said that during Father Gill's first curacy an imposing titled lady was inclined to telephone in a bullying tone and required to speak with nobody junior to the Vicar. Once in the Vicar's absence Father Colin took the call. "Are you one of the servants?" she asked.

His answer. "Yes, indeed; I am Father Gill, a curate." Thereafter the lady treated him with much respect.

Father Gill's concern for good order in all things was of course well known at his church in Brighton—St. Martin's—as also was his interest in good food, and his care that it should whenever possible be on hand.

But the gift for ordering ceremonies, and for introducing ceremony where it was wrongly lacking, made him a natural successor to Father Fynes-Clinton at S. Magnus the Martyr, London Bridge. It is said that one day not many years ago, a Roman Catholic Priest brought two of his servers to look around the church and was overheard explaining: "This is how it used to be with us, and how it always ought to be". There is also a tale about the last Bishop of London, Gerald Ellison. He came to Father Colin's church and is supposed to have remarked: "Don't you think the time has come to try and bring S. Magnus more into line with the tradition of the Church of England?" Father Colin agreed, but asked if His Lordship had anything particular in mind. "Perhaps a start could be made by switching from Latin to English for Benediction".

Father Colin's concern for the good ordering of events combined with reasonable comfort for those taking part became clear quite soon after his installation as Master. Guardians' Chapter meetings were soon removed from the All Souls' Chapel to the College Refectory, for the convenience of smokers.

It was at Father Colin's suggestion, indeed, that when the present Administrator was installed, this should be done formally, publicly and with a dash of style. Under him, too, Chapters of the Clerks and Dames became that much better ordered. The departure of Father Alan Carefull from the Administrator's stall was likewise made an occasion which was used to express everyone's deep gratitude for his work. There had, of course, been no formal departure in that sense either for Father Patten, or for his successor Father Colin Stephenson, both of whom died in office. But Father Charles Smith's departure from the Administrator's Cottage to the Vicarage of S. Mary Magdalen's in Beaumont Street, Oxford, was allowed to pass with little or no ceremony at all.

Father Colin, a stickler for etiquette, introduced some minor but significant details into the Guardians' Chapter proceedings. In place of the hurly-burly of the sacristy known in Father Stephenson's day, the Master has on each occasion bowed gravely to the Chapter at the start of proceedings, and bade farewell to each Guardian in turn with a Kiss of Peace at the close. It is to the retiring Master that we all owe the new practice of including in the *Mirror* a short summary of Chapter proceedings. He felt this was 'proper' as well as a prudent counter to the unbridled circulation of rumour.

To the unity of the Chapter he has been devoted; indeed unity among the Guardians has been a major concern throughout his term. It is always easy for sincere people with their nose to the parochial grindstone to observe their own sphere of work, and ignore wider considerations or the spheres of others. Here is the breeding-ground of minor differences, say on some contemporary church controversy, which could lead to real divisions of opinion among the Guardians. The same is true of the broad body of Walsingham supporters. Father Colin has been tireless in seeking to mend fences among Shrine supporters where this or that group have felt the Administration was either becoming 'too hard-line R.C.' or 'too moderate' according to the viewers' perspective. In the same way he has exerted all his diplomatic gifts—laced as ever with humour, even if a little sharpish on occasion—to ensure that the Guardians cherish and cultivate a common mind and above all follow Father Patten's plea that they keep the Shrine clear of current church controversy. (Older Guardians will remember Father Patten's strenuous pleas in this sense at the time of the South India Reunion Scheme.)

Two particular memories remain with this writer. There was a meeting on the final night of the Church Union Jubilee Eucharistic Congress at the Albert Hall. The President of the day was really not up to the occasion and in the final moments the event looked like becoming something of a flop after the whole audience had risen to acclaim Father Patten. At the psychologically critical moment Father Colin, as Church Union Chairman at that time, displaying all the scale and power of his personality, strode to the microphone to deliver a few vivid sentences about Our Lord's presence on the Eucharistic Altar. In the flick of a second the mood was raised to a level that will never be forgotten.

Then there was the Jubilee at Walsingham last October, and the all-night vigil. Father Colin's Mystery is the Ascension, he carried his bearers with him into the Seventh Heaven as if he was speaking poetry that poured from his heart—it led us to catch a glimpse of the glory to be revealed.

Patrick, Earl of Lauderdale.

Jack Banson
died 9 December 1978

It is the glory of this village that through all the events of the last half century, through the revival that has made it once more England's Nazareth, that has once more taken its name far and wide over the world, it has been not unresponsive to the Word of God in our midst.

Jack Banson was a true son of Norfolk and of this village, where he was born, and this was the place where he was brought up. He lived through all these events, he is one of our last links with those early days when Father Hope Patten was used by God to bring men back to Walsingham. It must have been all to easy in those days to remain sceptical and critical—we know there were many such, some of them in high places. It is still possible to criticise. But Jack, along with George Long, William Frary and the others saw with the eye of faith. Perhaps they did not see altogether where it was leading (faith is like that: you cannot know where it will take you); perhaps they were just doing what the Vicar wanted, but they were caught up in something bigger than they realised. Jack became a foundation Guardian of the Shrine of Our Lady of Walsingham in 1931, and continued so until 1976, and he was churchwarden of the parish from 1930 to 1967, and Colin Stephenson, in his book about it all, mentions the important people who were connected with the work, and speaks of them as "together with a small band of locals" forming the first members of the College Guardians. I would suggest that the "small band of locals" was, and is, as important as dukes and prelates, and to them, to Jack especially, for he has outlived them all, many thousands owe a deep debt of gratitude, and they hope that Walsingham will go on giving us such men of faith.

For it is as a man of faith that I think of Jack Banson, of that gentleness, stability and courtesy that go with faith. He was, if you like, a stick in the mud, he had no wider ambitions than his job in Barclays Bank. Perhaps he was true Norfolk in that, but in our world which seems dominated by pushers and go-getters, we need the reminder, the protest, which men like Jack give us. The practice of the Christian religion seemed perfectly natural and real to him, without any sense of it being superimposed on a half believing Englishman. It enabled him to bear great sorrow: he was church-warden when S Mary's burnt down, and I saw him frequently at the time of the death of his sister Mabel, with whom he lived. It enabled him to accept the loneliness which came after that, and the limitations and weaknesses of old age. When last I saw him at Aylsham, he was quite himself, and I am sure continued to be so until the end. He served God quietly and unobtrusively, he enjoyed his quiet pleasures—going to the Oxford Stores and meeting his friends—and in doing what has become part, a very important part, of the history of the Church in this land. He would not have realised this, but so it is. For Walsingham is one of the places where the spiritual revival and renewal for which we hope and pray, and of which there are already some signs, are taking place. It is important that Walsingham and all it stands for and has to give should play its part in the life of the Church, but to do that, it must be at peace in itself, and Jack, as church-warden of this parish which he loved, and Guardian of its shrine, represented something which must not disappear. To have the village invaded by thousands of people calls for patience and tolerance and kindness, for pilgrims have their all too human side. But it calls also for the quality of faith which we found in Jack Banson and in others like him. May it ever continue among us, that those who come here may learn not only—not so much—by buildings and images, by sermons and services, but by living, believing Christian men and women, what God can do for those who love him. For them, God has prepared good things that pass man's understanding, and may Jack, of the goodness and mercy of God, and at the prayers of Our Lady of Walsingham, enter into that inheritance.

Charles Smith

Alban Henry Baverstock, Priest

Vicar of Hinton Martel 1899–1930.
died 25 April 1950

I FIRST met Father Baverstock in the Clergy House at Holy Cross, S. Pancras, then in the Cartwright Gardens, when I was serving my title under his brother. He came to lunch and seemed to radiate a happy joyful atmosphere. That impression deepened during the subsequent years that it has been my privilege to know and claim him as a personal friend. In those days he was organising and developing the Holy Family Homes from Hinton Martel, which homes he and Father F. E. Baverstock and others founded. These have since grown into the homes of S. Nicholas; yet perhaps our own home of S. Hilary may really claim to be the one true representative of the old foundation, since it started as such in Cornwall and then was transferred to Walsingham.

Father became a regular pilgrim to the Shrine directly the revival began and in 1922 it was he who blessed, in the South Porch of the Parish Church, the now much venerated image of O.L.W., on that wonderful evening of July 6th. He preached the oration in S. Mary's on the occasion of the opening of the Holy House—that was in 1931 and became one of the foundation Fellows of the College of the Guardians of the Holy House established at that time, and in consequence he has been connected with the Shrine and its works ever since. It is not however his connection with Walsingham that will keep his name alive so much as his courage and erudition in maintaining the Catholic Faith both by pen and word of mouth. He has, indeed, during the whole of his long ministry, been a real "defender of the faith," meriting that title which was ill advisedly granted to one whose work has made the Catholic revival so necessary in these provinces.

Many a soul is grateful for his sound and painstaking spiritual guidance through long periods. All over the Anglican Communion, Catholics know his name and bear it in great respect, while those who knew him personally will always hold it in loving memory and veneration.

Mass was solemnly sung in the Pilgrimage Church on the day of his funeral, and all friends of Walsingham will add his name to their prayers and seek Our Lady's intercession for him, whose name, under the title of Walsingham, he invoked at the moment of his passing. May he rest in peace.

A. H. P.

Francis Edwin Baverstock, Priest

died 22 December 1952

On the Monday before Christmas Father Francis Baverstock died at the Clergy House, Notting Dale—still in harness at 79, as we are sure he would have wished. Father was an Honorary Guardian of the Holy House, but apart from that he had close connections with Walsingham for nearly 45 years. Father Reeves, the predecessor of the present Vicar, was a great friend of Father Baverstock, and gave him his title at Islington. Then, when at Holy Cross, S. Pancras, Father F. E. B. gave Father Hope Patten his title. While he was a deacon there in 1914 he was shown a small image of our Lady and Father Baverstock said "This is for Walsingham"—it was a present to Father Reeves who, just before he left Walsingham in 1920, put it on a bracket in the Lady Chapel. It now stands over the High Altar of the Parish Church.

Father had often preached his clear, simple gospel sermons at the Parish Mass, and was much loved in this Norfolk village by those who knew him.

He expressed a wish to be buried among us and this was done on 27th December. Francis Baverstock is one of the last of a body of great Parish Priests of the Subtractarian School—which were men who made the best of what the Catholic Revival is today. Indeed we live on their sowing—he was always interested in "developments," somewhat impatient of certain innovations—but always willing to help if real hard work was being done for souls.

He was a Priest Associate of the Holy House from the beginning and had a great love for the Shrine and its Children's Home.

Walter Gervase Bennett, Priest

Vicar of the Church of the Annunciation
Marble Arch London 1947–76
died 16 October 1976

It is impossible to think of him or speak of him without a smile of joy: to be with him was always a joy, and after a few minutes, nearly always laughter. One thinks of his marvellous sense of humour and of the ridiculous.

I remember not many years ago, going with him to Gubbio in Umbria and walking up to the shrine of S. Ubaldo, Patron of the city, at the top of the small mountain above the town (Father Bennett was always very excited by holy corpses—an excitement which I could never share to the same extent!). It was stupid of us to walk up in the heat when there was a funicular railway—but we did and then afterwards decided to descend in the funicular. This proved to be a series of metal baskets which never stopped but continued to proceed like a conveyor belt. You had to jump on and shut the bar and stand two at a time in the basket. Almost immediately we found ourselves going over a precipice into mid-air. I was very alarmed and clutched my hat and book exclaiming loudly. Father Bennett was pealing with laughter, first at my unnecessary alarm and secondly at the whole situation—two elderly Anglican Clergymen gliding down the side of an Italian mountain in this absurd vehicle. We think of Father

Bennett's childlike joy at being introduced unexpectedly to the Pope on a Parish Pilgrimage to Rome. We think of his love of beauty; his love of Italy; of the piano (in particular the music of Chopin, Rachmaninov, Ravel and the great Beethoven); of his love of flowers of which he had considerable knowledge; of his making beautiful things for the church; of his love of reading biographies. We think too of his carefully prepared and beautifully expressed sermons and magazine articles, of his great love for Catholic worship and ceremonial. We think too of his wonderful love of people. How gentle and patient he was with old people. How he loved children. For many years he produced that lovely Nativity Play in his church and he always took immense trouble with the school in this parish. He had great courage; many times he faced very difficult situations indeed during his incumbency here and managed them superbly; and latterly he suffered considerable pain and was always cheerful about it. And what marvellous faith he had. His was an absolutely straight forward, and in the true and profound sense, simple faith. He had a habit of talking about his relations and friends as though he thought one knew them as well as he did—and very soon one did because of his great gift of story telling and of describing characters. He would talk of his departed relations and friends as though they were still visibly here, they were always with him and somehow he seemed to know what life after death was like.

He had, as we know, a deep devotion to Our Lady and to her Shrine at Walsingham of which he was a Guardian.

He was able to hear those of you who were with him on his last pilgrimage praying and singing at the second Station of the Cross below his bedroom window. Soon afterwards he was asleep and though he woke briefly, he then lapsed into unconsciousness.

Martin Gibbs

Sir John Best-Shaw, Baronet
died 26 February 1984

Sir John Best-Shaw was the last surviving member of the original Guardians of the Holy House, appointed by Fr. Hope Patten in 1931. It is only 6 years since he resigned and became a Guardian Emeritus.

Devotion to our Lady was a very real and important part of his religion, and to be a Guardian was to him no sinecure. He took an active interest in all the affairs of the Shrine and visited it frequently. History relates that, in years gone by, he could be very much the Naval Officer at Chapter Meetings, and that nothing was allowed to escape his eagle eye. His enthusiasm for the Shrine was infectious and meant a great deal in the days when it was less "popular" than it is now. It would be hard to reckon now how many pilgrims paid their first visit, how many parishes made their first weekend pilgrimage, because he urged them to. He accompanied some of the latter to see that they did it properly.

The singing of the *"Dies irae"* during the Requiem for him at S Stephen's , Gloucester Road would have given him great pleasure. It brought to my mind another Requiem sung at S Mary's Swanley (the church built by his father) over 30 years previously at the time of the death of King George VI. The singer of the Sequence on that occasion was Sir John himself at what was otherwise the ordinary School Mass of the Junior School.

His action made a considerable im-

Sir John (on the right) with Major Bowker and Sir William Milner (centre) in 1938.

pression on the few adults present, and was typical of the humble and whole-hearted way in which he threw himself into the life of the church which he was then attending. Other churches which he attended during his War service say the same kind of thing about him. When he moved to Boxley in 1956, he showed equal care and loyalty for his church there, though it was far from being an "Anglo-Catholic" shrine at that time. But he was well able to express his enthusiasm for the full Catholic faith without being "off-putting" to others.

He had learned the Faith from his father, and it was all so natural to him.

He reminded me once, and it was a salutary reminder, of the difficulty that he and people brought up like him had in adapting to such practices as the relaxation of the Rules of Fasting Communion. In his younger days he said, he had endured a lot from such things as the raised eyebrows and acid remarks of those who thought him very odd to insist on going to "early Service". Having persisted in doing so, he was not prepared easily to change his habits.

Nevertheless his charity and humility would never allow him openly to criticise others. It was this charity and humility that made him so welcome a guest in every house and parsonage in which he stayed. He once caused some consternation to the man of the household when he surprised him in the act of performing some menial task. "Oh, I do that in my house every Saturday" he at once exclaimed, and all embarrassment ceased.

His enthusiasms were those of a simple, single-minded Christian. Whether he was advocating the Church Union, Walsingham or the Additional Curates Society he was hard to resist. The same unaffected Christian simplicity enabled him to be obviously pleased and even proud at being made High Sheriff of Kent, without being conceited or pompous about it.

But Christianity begins at home. Typically there was always a Crib in front of the Christmas Tree at Boxley Abbey. Sir John's true spirit was manifested in his pride and care for his Christian family and in the loyalty and love they gave him in return.

C. H. Nixon

Major Arthur Frank Bowker

died 12 June 1950

He was one of Foundation Fellows of the College of the Guardians of the Holy House, being elected in 1931.

To quote from another notice of his passing he was an "engineer, scientist, explorer and artilleryman." Among his outstanding achievements he built the first railway to Jerusalem and was one of the original geological party to discover gold in Klondike. He was a great traveller, having visited all the countries of the world.

Deeply impressed by the Spiritual Exercises of S. Ignatius, he determined to spread the knowledge of the Manresa in this country, and so he founded the Society of Retreat Conductors, giving the land and raising the necessary buildings at Stacklands, in Kent. Moreover, he built and furnished the Chapel of SS. Thomas and Philip in the Pilgrimage Church. This he did to the honour of Our Lady and in memory of two of his great friends, Father Wilmot-Philips and Father Arthur Tooth. The latter had a great devotion to S. Thomas of Canterbury, and one of his great desires was to re-erect his Shrine in the Trinity Chapel of Canterbury Cathedral; indeed plans for this were being prepared, but the offer was rejected. It was through a happy coincidence when a relic of this Martyr was given to the Shrine that this was placed in a feretory beneath the altar beside which Father Tooth's effigy lies. The Major always persevered in whatever he undertook. He frequently cycled from Kent to Walsingham, even when he was nearing his 80th year, in these latter days. In order to avoid the traffic of London he pedalled to the Shrine and back via the South Coast, skirting the border of Wales! Always a keen Catholic, a personal friend of Dr. Pusey, in whose house he passed much of his youth, he had a great devotion to Our Lady and her Sanctuary at Walsingham and a lively interest in all the works connected with it.

Henry Joy Fynes-Clinton, Priest

Rector of S. Magnus the Martyr, London Bridge
1922–59

died 4 December 1959

The death of Father Fynes-Clinton at the advanced age of 84, though not un-expected, came as a shock to his many friends and indeed all who loved and knew him so well for so many years. Born 84 years ago, his long life covered a period in which the Catholic Movement had to face and overcome many trials and much opposition until it consolidated itself and secured toleration. In recent years he often spoke of the difficulties encountered in that period and of the outstanding figures in the Movement, nearly all of whom he knew or had come into contact with.

His knowledge of the Orthodox Church was not confined to Russia alone as the Greek and Serbian decorations which he received bear witness to. For his work on behalf of the Serbian Ortho-dox Church he received an Archpriest's cross and later that also of the Russian Church.

His work in connection with the Re-

Of his work and *love* for the restoration of the Shrine of Our Lady of Walsingham there is little need to speak. During the latter part of his life this occupied a large part of his time and attention. Again as Director of the Catholic League for many years his work is well known.

Of the Church of St. Magnus-the-Martyr, which he beautified, and which was so much a part of him, and the earlier difficulties which he had in connection with the Protestant opposition, all is well known. But when these difficulties were over, the church became a well-known centre and spiritual home for many people. Under its shelter many activities were given a generous welcome and a home. He refounded the ancient City Guild of Our Lady of Salve Regina.

For the ancient City of London and all that it stood for he had the most profound interest and a wide knowledge. He was on excellent terms with the City and served in several clerical capacities such as Lord Mayor's Chaplain. He himself was not only Chaplain to but a Past Master of the Worshipful Company of Plumbers. He also initiated in recent years a group of Catholic Members of Parliament interested in Walsingham, to whom he acted as Chaplain. His indeed was a very full life.

Ivan Young

union Movement in so far as the Roman Catholic Church is concerned was persistent and extensive. He both knew and was on excellent terms with many Roman Catholic Clergy and abroad he was well known and respected. In connection with this he conducted an immense correspondence, the extent of which was quite astounding. For many years he fostered and took a deep interest in the Church Unity Octave.

Philip Harold Husbands, Priest

Rector of S. James Wednesbury 1946–80

died 5 October 1987

The passing of Philip Husbands severs another earthly link with the early days of the Shrine's revival. He first came upon it soon after the rebuilding of the Holy House in 1931 when he was a student at the Tatterford Matriculation Col-

lege some eight miles away. He loved it ever after.

Trained at Mirfield, Philip exercised his ministry first in Newcastle upon Tyne and then at Tonge Moor in Bolton where he was often seen, in later years, visiting Auntie Pine who brought him up. During the War he was a Naval Chaplain.

His most notable work, however, was done at S James's Wednesbury where he was instituted in 1946 and where he remained until retirement. Pilgrims and others would testify to the influence he exercised there and to the esteem in which he was held. The present writer well remembers preaching for the patronal festival in 1978 when a packed church looked splendid and colourful. Philip presided looking wonderfully magisterial and sounding colossal as only he could. The whole evening is an abiding memory.

Longevity was a feature of Philip's ministry: long at Wednesbury, long in Convocation and General Synod he was also long a Guardian of the Holy House, being installed by Father Patten in 1957. It was at Chapters that his years' long knowledge of Walsingham proved so useful and where his devotion to the place became so evident. And what a sturdy support he was to successive Administrators!

He was much missed when increasing age and infirmity obliged him to resign his stall a year or so ago and his considerable presence was no longer visible. His last years were spent in the Charterhouse. A Londoner by birth he returned thither in retirement.

Readers who knew and loved him might treasure this glimpse of him. It was in the summer of 1946, before he went to Wednesbury and when he was looking after the interregnum at S John's Tue Brook, Liverpool that he was seen from a passing tram making his way very purposefully towards the church. He looked like a wonderful blend of a lion, a bull mastiff and an angel—an unforgettable sight. It was an unforgettable service that followed in that magnificent church with Philip's voice echoing round it and uncompromising assertions about the faith sounding forth.

He was a good priest. We thank God for his life and ministry and wish him all joy in his Risen Lord.

Uvedale Lambert
died 15 September 1983

Uvedale had that attractive, contagious quality which made me realise that he was one of the rather small band of human beings in whom the image of their Creator has not been defaced or tarnished. That is what goodness means to me. Having said that, Uvedale was no plastic saint. He was a real man, living the Christian life in a real world, with a delicious sense of humour. Of the hundreds of happy human memories I give you two:

I had been at South Park convalescing after an operation. On the day I was due to return to Bishop's House, Uvedale came to my bedroom in full hunting kit to apologise for not being available to see me off later in the morning as he was otherwise engaged. As was his wont, he asked my blessing. As my views on blood sports were different from his, I said "Well only half a blessing today Uvedale". An hour or two later he was thrown from his horse. As he fell he was heard to say "Blast the Bishop"—indeed there was an alternative adjective before the word "bishop". And I well remember as many of you will, that as High Sheriff of Surrey in full regalia he had to be pushed from function to function in a chair—and he invariably blamed me for his infirmity.

There was another occasion, the memory of which I treasure. We were on our way to the Shrine of Our Lady at Walsingham in Norfolk, of which Uvedale was a Guardian. Walsingham meant a great deal to him. The time came for lunch and I insisted on being host. At home Mel kept him strictly to a vegetar-

99

ian diet, nut, lettuce, scraped carrot, cottage cheese and worse. I passed him the menu: he said "Smoked Salmon, fillet steak, Pêche Melba and a bottle of claret. But you must promise not to tell Mel."

Well, there you are, this loving and lovable Uvedale, this child of God, this so very human being. And how did it come about? Quite simply, he was like Barnabas "full of the Holy Spirit and of faith". The little chapel that adjoins South Park is the outward sign of Uvedale's inner strength. Day by day he and Mel said morning and evening prayer and whenever possible met at the altar for the sacrament. And there were the times in the day for silent prayer. Uvedale was indeed a man of faith. Although an Anglican who loved his catholic inheritance, he transcended denominational or party barriers, and in his earlier years he found inspiration in the Focolare movement while he himself inspired the lay community that took root at South Park, and which encompassed

him with its love and prayers in his last days.

No wonder such a man added many people to the Church. But let the last words be not mine, but Uvedale's. They are to be found in a series of talks that Uvedale read to a group of Christians in America in 1948—nearly 40 years ago: it is the final paragraph of the talk:

"The answer then to the question 'so what?', which I would like to suggest to you and leave with you as a last word, is just this. Union with God is our aim. It can and should begin here and now, and leads us through the gate of death to the nearer presence, where we shall know even as we are known. The Christian religion is not for this life only. But it gives us certain rules and certain helps for this life. The greatest of prayers is the corporate worship of God in the Eucharist where we are in the closest touch with our Blessed Lord. This is our standard, this is our criterion, this is our touchstone, and the earnest of our salvation."

Bishop Mervyn Stockwood

Derrick Albert Lingwood, Priest

died 5 April 1972

Derrick Albert Lingwood, priest and bursar of the Shrine of Our Lady of Walsingham, died suddenly at Withycombe Raleigh, bringing to an end an era in the history of the revival.

Every age seems to raise up outstanding men able to meet the challenge of the times, and by some special providence Derrick was brought to prominence during the early years of the restoration.

Derrick was born in Walsingham on 17th March, 1910, to Albert and Alice Lingwood, local business people. He was the eldest of six children. From an early age he developed a strong sense of vocation and about 1925 went to live at

the vicarage so that the Vicar, Fr. Hope Patten, could direct his studies for the priesthood. In return he was to assist Hope Patten with his business and financial interests. Like so many men of genius and vision Hope Patten had no head for money matters, and Derrick's remarkable talent for business and finance was put to good use. So began a partnership which at times seemed inspired.

The Shrine was first set up in the Guild Chapel of St. Mary's where Derrick was a server. It was a humble affair at first, but quickly gained support, and as its influence spread so the work increased and Derrick became indispens-

able to the Vicar. By 1930 the revival had become something of an ecclesiastical thorn in the diocese. Pressure from the Bishop and a genuine apprehension for its future stability convinced those responsible that the Shrine should be moved to a new site where the freehold was owned independently of ecclesiastical authority. Clearly these years were the proving ground for Derrick, the time when he grew in stature and laid the foundations to his many achievements in later life.

Around 1931 the need for a body of Trustees became evident, so as to ensure the continuity of the Shrine and give it the corporate backing necessary to its continued growth. The College of Guardians therefore came into being, consisting of 12 priests and 8 laymen. Derrick was one of the founder members and became the first bursar at the age of twenty-one. 1934 was another landmark, being the year he was ordained priest by Bishop Blunt of Bradford, serving his title at Holy Trinity. Bradford.

Under the impetus of the Catholic movement enthusiasm for the Shrine knew no bounds and the development gathered pace. Considerable property was obtained in the village, and not unnaturally Derrick's responsibilities multiplied since all this had to be maintained, and much of it was in poor condition. It was not easy to find the necessary capital to keep pace with each new venture, but somehow the voracious demand was satisfied. He showed considerable adroitness in side-stepping the more extravagant ideas put forward—always a pitfall for the unwary bursar!

In 1939 Fr. Bernard Walke invited the Guardians to take over the maintenance of a small orphanage he had started in St. Hilary's. Cornwall, and this project became the Shrine charity. Much work devolved on Derrick as the honorary secretary and treasurer with responsibility for raising money and meeting bills. Neither was this made easier during the war years when East Anglia was declared a closed area with its restriction on movement. Like a runaway horse there was no stopping the headlong pursuit for new undertakings, regardless of whether the organisation was equipped to cope. From 1944 to 1958 an attempt was made to found a Shrine choir school, and this particular project was to give Derrick many sleepless nights. The experiment was doomed to failure. Lack of sufficient capital at the right time and a crisis of personalities proved too strong a combination even for Derrick's financial expertise.

Hope Patten was a man of vision and equipped with the necessary determination to succeed against all opposition— the Shrine would not have been restored without his creative impulse and drive— but there can be no doubt that had it not been for Derrick's skill and steadying influence the ship could well have foundered on more than one financial rock. In so many ways he was the perfect foil to Hope Patten, and this is well illustrated by the story of a local man who had been worsted in a business deal: "Patten and Lingwood parsons? More like b__ solicitors! For what one b__ doesn't think of the other one does".

As assistant priest he was particularly active too, being pastorally responsible for the two daughter churches, as well as assisting the Vicar at St. Mary's combined with his duties at the Shrine as priest and bursar. And it must have taken great courage to continue his ministry for so long amongst his own people. The Establishment failed to understand the significance of Walsingham, still less the need for such exotic practices; it was hardly likely therefore, that the Vicar would be allowed a curate. Derrick was therefore supernumerary for many years and received board and accommodation, and what amounted to pocket money for his enormous labours.

It was typical of him that on his day off he busied himself in public work, and for many years and until he left Walsingham served as a District Councillor and was Chairman of the Housing Committee. With so many "hats" it was not surprising that by the middle 50s he was exhausted, mentally and physically. He had been bursar for 25 years and the strain of his many duties was becoming intolerable. Also his churchmanship in tune with the times, had begun to develop a less inflexible attitude than that of Hope Patten, and he was convinced it would be morally wrong to stay.

He left Walsingham in 1956 to take charge of the Devonshire parish of St. Martin's, Barton. However, this did not end his association with the Shrine for he remained a director until the end of his life.

There is in the campanile at Walsingham a bell given by Derrick and dedicated to his patron saint, St. Patrick. Posterity will surely honour his memory (as we do) for the part he played in the restoration of the Shrine he loved, and may we hope that Patrick's voice will be a constant reminder to us all to pray for his soul.

Stanley Smith

The engraved glass window in the chapel of the Crowning with Thorns is a memorial to him.

Sir William Milner

died 29 March 1960

Sir William Milner, of Appletrewick, Skipton, the renowned architect, and one of the re-founders of the Shrine of Our Lady of Walsingham, died at the age of sixty-six.

His enormous figure will be best remembered in relation to the Shrine of Our Lady of Walsingham. To the Mother of God he had, since youth, a deep and quiet devotion, a quality which marked his life in other respects—his passion for flowers, especially rare rock plants, his quiet enjoyment of the Yorkshire moors where he made his home, the solace that he found in solitude.

He first met the Rev. A. Hope Patten in 1924 and through the friendship which they quickly formed he became, almost literally, the re-founder of the Shrine of Our Lady. Milner had promised Fr. Patten material support in his endeavours to revive devotion, which began by restoring an image of Our Lady to the parish church.

When in due time the Bishop of Norwich required it to be removed, he agreed that it could be housed in a special church built for the purpose, and what is now considered to be a revival of a Royal peculiar of the Middle Ages went forward.

The problem was to find a site, the more so as land in the village was scarce and the original site of the shrine was not known. In the event some allotment grounds came into the market and were bought by Milner. When work began on restoring the Holy House, foundations that corresponded exactly to Erasmus's description of the original shrine were found.

Milner, although he believed these to be the original foundations, was too careful an antiquary to assert that there was any proof of this; but one of the great joys that sustained his subsequent life was the conviction that he had been the instrument of buying back for God's use ground hallowed after the Vision of Richeldis in 1061.

That he should not have been allowed to live for the ninth centenary seems strange to the rest of us; but he lived to see such great advances that as he looked back on nearly thirty years' work for Walsingham he stood amazed. His firm were architects for the Shrine church, a building of great beauty; yet at the time the Holy House was restored some questioned whether they ought even to build its outer covering to the roof-height of the church intended to re-

Sir William Milner with Bracken.

103

place it. He found the money for that and it was he who urged the church should be as large as it was. A year ago he was discussing how it could now be doubled in size and blaming his own lack of vision for consenting in the 'thirties to something so small.

His home at Percevall Hall, on the Yorkshire moors, was ever intended as a sort of retreat. He found the buildings, as a derelict grange of Fountains Abbey, restored them with consummate taste, added a chapel, and surrounded it all with one of the most extraordinary rock gardens in West Europe. From rough moorland he grew fine trees and gracious flowers. They symbolised what lay nearest his heart, a profound devotion to the Lord and to his Mother.

Patrick, Earl of Lauderdale

Hubert Adderley, Lord Norton

died 17 February 1961

The rise and growth of the restored devotion to Our Lady of Walsingham was something which Hubert Adderley, Lord Norton, had seen practically from the beginning; and to him it meant a very great deal. In the early years, when he was living in Norfolk, he often visited Walsingham; and he early became a Guardian. He continued to have a great and deepening appreciation of what Walsingham means. It formed a very important part of his life. He has himself related the story of the pilgrimage he made at a time when it appeared more than possible that Lady Norton might lose her sight, and how there was a complete cure.

He came latterly each year with the Birmingham pilgrimage as well as that of S. John's Coventry (and nearly always paid a visit to the Boys' Home); he practically never failed to attend meetings as a Guardian, and was always ready to speak or preside at meetings to promote devotion to Our Lady. He also enjoyed being able sometimes to come for a few days quietly and just be at peace there.

But what manner of man was he? What lay behind that quiet and courteous exterior? He was a man of strong character, who would hold firmly to what he believed to be right. He had a particular sense of the value of the sacrament of penance, and of devotion to Our Lady as safeguarding the truth of the Incarnation. He held most tenaciously to what he called "my half-hour" (of meditation) without which he said the day was all wrong; and came to have a great love of the psalms. He particularly disliked fuss and ostentation and loved simplicity.

E. H. W. Crusha

Vivan Albertus Petersen, Priest

died 9 September 1966

Canon Vivan Albertus Petersen, D.D., known to his friends as "Pete", was a great figure in the Catholic Movement in America. He was the Rector of St. James', Cleveland, Ohio, and he maintained it as a Catholic stronghold in a Diocese which is almost entirely Protestant. But he had a great influence in the Church at large and he was so much responsible for persuading the Benedictines of Nashdom to make a foundation in America that he was affectionately known as the Godfather of the Monks at St. Gregory's Priory, Three Rivers. He came to Walsingham in the early days of the restoration of the Shrine and became its life-long supporter and generous benefactor. He was one of the first Honorary Guardians and it was to him that Fr. Patten wrote during the War urging that if the Shrine and everyone here were destroyed Pete must immediately start raising money in America and undertake to see that it was restored at once. Fr. Patten obviously regarded him as a miracle man, for having said that he never hoped to get a relic of St. Thomas of Canterbury. Pete, through his wide Roman Catholic connections, promptly obtained one and sent it over for the Shrine. When he retired from St. James', Cleveland, they erected a splendid Shrine of Our Lady of Walsingham as a thanksgiving for his rectorship.

On 9th September, 1966, he died suddenly and was buried at St. Gregory's Priory, close to which he was planning to build himself a house. At the Shrine there was a High Mass of Requiem and a sense of deep loss in the passing of a generous and affectionate friend.

Arthur Smallwood, O.B.E.

died 9 March 1938

Mr. Smallwood had been a Guardian of the Shrine for nearly two years before his death, and the news of his serious illness came as a shock to all who knew him. From 1921–1934 he had been director of Greenwich Hospital and it was owing to his energy and zeal that the Royal Hospital School for the sons of Naval men was built at Holbrook overlooking the River Stour, and the boys transferred there.

"The central feature of the School is its magnificent Chapel, dedicated to our Lady and S. Nicholas. This lovely and stately modern Church, with its dignified High Altar standing before an Apse, resplendent with a unique representation in mosaics of the Nativity of our Lord, was very dear to the heart of Arthur Smallwood, for there in the daily pleading of the Holy Sacrifice was to be the consecration of all the activities of the School."

The bell of this great Chapel was baptized by Bishop O'Rorke in the Shrine of our Lady at Walsingham. Great personal devotion to our Lady was the keynote of Arthur Smallwood's life, and he was overjoyed when asked to join the College of the Guardians of the Holy House. His last visit to the Shrine was in the Summer of 1937.

John Herbert Cloete Twisaday, Priest

Vicar of All Saints Notting Hill 1932–61
died 18 January 1971

The saga of the former Vicar of All Saints', Notting Hill has been faithfully told by himself, in a well-known little publication written after his retirement in 1961. Here is a portrait, rather impressionist, of the Father towards the end.

John Twisaday had been reared in an age which respected and kept significant objects; and so he carried with him into retirement the accoutrements of his former career. He would open the great red front door of 90 St. Mark's Road to confront the visitor, still soutaned and even birettaed, and always remained a vicar-figure, a professional.

The visitor—and he welcomed so many—will remember the curiosity of each singular ornament in the house, from the vintage visiting-cards in the hall, next to the large collection of snuff-boxes, to the letter from one Bishop Roncalli still displayed above the chimney-piece in the drawing-room.

Here was a well preserved, shrewd and urbane priest who could never have retired, in the worldly sense; and so he made sure that he did not. In his own house he could step into church: the chapel at the front of No. 90 being furnished to the hilt, to the very collection bags. Beyond his own home, of course, there was always the priestly and fraternal welcome at St. John's, Holland Road, and the Church of the Annunciation, Marble Arch. Father John's associations with the latter are well stated by Father Bennett in the Annunciation Magazine for March, 1971. At Holland Road, where he had served for a decade in the twenties, Father Twisaday was always warmly provided with priestly facilities and brotherhood—by no means the only priest to have received help and encouragements from its Vicar, Father Cyril Hordern. All this meant very much to him, and consoled him for having continued in life far beyond his time, as he would say with amusement. The writer remembers serving as a fellow-minister with Father John, meticulous as always, and so appreciative of being "useful", in the Holy Week at St. John's.

The Father's last visit to Walsingham, which gave us all a rare pleasure, ended his innumerable pilgrimages and visits. Father Bennett has referred to his immense devotion to Our Lady's Shrine; and when Father Charles entertained him specially in November, 1969, we were touched by the pathos of the occasion, which was obviously the last dinner-conversation we should all enjoy together. As the single tall candle burned at his Guardian's stall, so recently, in his memory the writer recalls the saying of a very elderly and faithful priest's housekeeper. "What made them so different, the priests of that time was that they were mostly *dear men*— we loved them".

William Mason

Edward Otway Humphrey Whitby, Priest

Vicar of S. Mary, Graham Street, Pimlico 1916–48

died 1948

It was a great shock and grief to hear of the sudden death of Father Whitby. He had been closely associated with the Shrine almost from the foundation of the College of Guardians of which he was a member. He was both a valued friend and a benefactor of the Sanctuary. He had a deep interest in Walsingham and its works, and, when he enjoyed better health, loved being at the Shrine.

Father Whitby was one of those fast disappearing Priests of the old school, a man of deep devotion and dignified, almost cold reserve, but beneath it was a warmth of heart and friendliness that was sometimes astounding. All who had the privilege of knowing him were conscious of his wisdom and discretion, and although many did not follow his lead in his liturgical convictions there was no one who had any association with him who could fail to love and admire him. On hearing the news of his death the big bell at the Shrine was tolled, as is our custom for Guardians, and a Requiem sung on the following Friday which coincided with a Priests' Pilgrimage.

The Order of the Living Rosary of Our Lady of Walsingham

When the Shrine was restored in 1922 a number of people, both natives of the village and many from outside, offered their services enthusiastically to promote and assist in the organization of pilgrimages. Some even uprooted themselves and came to live in Walsingham, the better to carry on the work which had become very dear to their hearts. Among these were a number of devoted women who gave unstintingly and without material reward of their talents in art and embroidery or in the more mundane but none the less important tasks of caring for the needs and comfort of the growing numbers of pilgrims.

In 1953 Father Hope Patten, the restorer of the Shrine, and first Master of the College of Guardians, felt that there should be some recognition of this work over the years. He therefore drew up a plan for such recognition and conferred an honour upon 6 ladies whose devotion to the Shrine had been outstanding. These were Miss Enid Chadwick, Mrs D R Ferrier, Mrs H G Brackley, the Reverend Mother Cicely SSM, Miss H Loddiges and Miss Doyle-Smythe. They were each presented with a gilded medallion having on it in blue enamel a figure of Our Lady of Walsingham and they were to be known as **Dames of the Shrine**.

Shortly before his death in 1958 Father Hope Patten had expressed the wish to extend this honour to certain priests and laymen who had also been active in promoting the work of the Shrine and encouraging pilgrimages to it. They would be known as **Clerks and Lay Clerks**. Sadly he was unable to carry this out and it was left to his successor, Father Colin Stephenson, the second Master, to bring it into effect. He conceived the idea of expanding the original plan of a mere decoration into something more permanent and in 1960 with the cordial approval of the College of Guardians he founded the **Sacred Order of the Living Rosary of Our Lady of Walsingham**. In thus basing it on the Holy Rosary it was the intention that there should be at least 15 members corresponding to the 15 Mysteries. There were to be at least 5 priests (Clerks), 5 Laymen (Lay Clerks) and 5 women who would have the title of Dames of the Order. The original 5 Dames were, under the new scheme, assigned the Glorious Mysteries. Each member, at his or her installation, is assigned to one of the 15 altars in the Shrine Church embodying all 15 Mysteries of the Rosary.

The insignia of the Order designed by Fr W. G. de Lara Wilson is as follows:
For Clerks A mozetta of blue silk, lined and edged with red and a ribbon of the same colours from which hangs a gilt cross with superimposed on it, an enamel medal in gold and red of Our Lady of Walsingham.
For Lay Clerks A sash of blue silk, lined and edged with red, to be worn on the left shoulder and under the right arm. In addition a ribbon and cross as those worn by Clerks.
For Dames A large bow of the ribbon as described above with a dependant medallion of Our Lady of Walsingham and a sash as worn by Lay Clerks.

This insignia is worn at the National Pilgrimage, at the Annual Chapter and whenever appropriate at other functions, at Walsingham or elsewhere, in honour of Our Lady.

Enid Mary Chadwick

died 24 October 1987

Enid Mary Chadwick had lived in Walsingham for well over fifty years. She had completely identified herself with all that it stands for, and it is difficult to think of it without her. She came here from Brighton in 1934. The daughter of a priest, she had been to a convent school in Oxford run by the Society of the Holy and Undivided Trinity, whose house is now S Antony's College. It was an old fashioned school, no doubt. Its curriculum was not designed to produce the career woman of today, but it had certainly borne the kind of fruit it desired in Enid. The standards and values by which things were judged remained with her all her life, though she was not by any means an ultra-conservative, opposed to all change in the Church and in society. In an age which has seen such revolutionary change in manners as in everything else, it is no small thing to have kept the faith, the manner of life to which one committed oneself in one's youth. Many a man and woman would

have been much happier had they done just that.

Her artistic ability was trained at the Brighton School of Art, but her life's work really began when she came to Walsingham in 1934. She could not have foreseen the next fifty years, the way in which she would become completely identified with this Shrine church, but she had just those abilities Father Hope Patten could use. He had a gift of identifying such qualities and drawing them out of people. Enid's painting and her personal style have made this Shrine church what it is, and her mark is everywhere. Della Robbia may have designed the Annunciation as you come in, but Enid Chadwick painted the copy which greets you. The reliquary of S Vincent may be modelled on that of S Ursula in Bruges, but it was Enid who conceived the designs and the heraldry which ornament it. The mysteries of the faith, the lives and legends of the saints are set before us in a way all can under-

stand. The simple, as in the middle ages she loved, learn directly from her paintings, and many who would be regarded as sophisticated in these matters, find that their unpretentious charm speaks to them as the children of God. Did she learn her love of heraldry from Hope Patten, or share it with him? Guardians come and go, but it is Enid's brush which records their names, amid all the heraldic symbols she could muster. Her puckish sense of humour accounts for many a little private joke in paint which even the subject may not have recognized. Her decoration is direct, and full of devotion; it may be derivative, but it has passed through the mind and hands of someone we all knew who had dedicated herself to this Shrine and its witness, and that witness will speak to many for years to come.

Known to a smaller number was her power as a caricaturist. Some of us have small collections of her cartoons which we will always treasure. Father Colin Stephenson, I know, considered that in some ways Enid had restricted herself by dedicating herself so completely to Walsingham. She had that sardonic, almost cynical, sense of humour, that minute observation, which make the cartoonist. Enid could have earned a great deal of money, and a very different reputation had she entered the field of journalism or commercial art, but this was the life she had chosen and loved.

One wondered at times if Enid was a lonely person, but was it not rather that loneliness which is part of the life of us all, and with which we must all come to terms? Yet she had many friends, and loved going to stay with them, and developing new friendships. She was to be seen at Walsingham gatherings all over the country, and people delighted to see her there—she was part of Walsingham. She loved parties, and invitations and the social life of this village in an almost girlish way. She loved the sights and sounds of the Norfolk countryside. After I had left here, I remember receiving each year a box of snowdrops in early spring and mushrooms in their season. Once when I lived here, my life was made intolerable until I had gone to see a flock of Egyptian cranes which had exceptionally settled in a field near Sandringham. But she loved equally the grander delights of London or Oxford—the concerts, the theatre and the ballet. She read widely, and enjoyed good conversation. At times her almost childish manner could annoy those more accustomed to the hurly burly of the world. Perhaps we need to listen to One who said that unless we become as little children we cannot enter into the kingdom of heaven. Behind all this and supporting it was a life of deep and dedicated prayer. It is no breach of confidence to say that in latter years it had become very largely a matter of remaining quietly in the presence of God, for that is the kind of prayer that comes to many older people. But she was faithful to it.

She lies here surrounded by her life's work, and no work could have been more single-minded. She has asked that on her monument should be inscribed the words: "Lord I have loved the habitation of thy house." And may the shadow and type she has loved here prove to be an anticipation of her delight in the presence of God, where Blessed Mary, Our Lady of Walsingham, and all the saints may be her companions for all eternity.

Charles Smith

Dorothy Ferrier

died 3 December 1972

For many years Dorothy Ferrier was a familiar part of the pilgrimage scene. In her dealings with people she could be very direct which at times made her a very formidable character, but one could not suppress a feeling of admiration and respect for her devotion to the cause, and the unflagging energy she gave to the work. Those who knew her really well could appreciate a subtle sense of humour which at times could be uncomfortably penetrating!

Dorothy came to Walsingham just before the War and this settled the question of who should run the Shrine Shop. She had only her time and service to offer and these she gave the Shrine abundantly for 27 years. The Shop was maintained in a dignified and grand manner which made one feel in her presence one should "stand in awe and sin not!" At the end of a tiring day Dorothy would retire to Stonegate House in Bridewell Street (site of the leper hospital and former police station), noted for its old-world character as much as the lack of comfort; the bathroom had to be navigated through a cupboard in the wall—since two cupboards adjoined it did not do to make a mistake! But she loved every inch of it and was grateful for the solitude and shelter it gave her.

It is difficult to realise her life covered the reigns of six kings and queens. As a young girl she must have been excited by news of the Boer War, and saddened by the dreadful carnage of two world wars which decimated Europe and changed the pattern of life for ever. So much had happened in Walsingham that it can hardly have seemed the same place to which she came in days before the War. A staunch supporter of the Anglo-Catholic movement which was a decisive influence on her, she came to accept liturgical innovations as inevitable, if sometimes of dubious necessity. But nothing could shake her faith and discipline.

Dorothy's vitality was remarkable for an octogenarian, but the Jubilee Year was a particularly strenuous time, and it was a great relief when she retired in October 1972. She mourned the parting but accepted it as the practical thing to do. She was thrilled when Bishops, Lords and Commoners gathered at Stonegate House for a farewell party: it was a happy and memorable occasion which gave her considerable pleasure. Since the Shrine Shop was her life and service it was perhaps inevitable (and providential) the end should come so soon after retirement. Dorothy was not afraid of approaching death, but living alone at such times can be a problem. Her last

111

illness made it necessary to consult the doctor—not so much for medication as to ensure there would be "no unpleasantness when I die".

Lawrence Goodrich Harding, Priest

Vicar of Saint Alban the Martyr, Bordesley, Birmingham, 1953–81

died 23 March 1981

Although Canon Harding was ordained in 1941 his entry in Crockford occupies no more than three-quarters of an inch. He had, in fact, had only two jobs—curate of S Mary the Virgin, Kenton and then Vicar of S Alban's Birmingham.

A ministry of close on 30 years in one parish is in itself remarkable in these days and gives a very clear indication of Father Harding's character and temperament. No doubt he could have moved on several times and received distinguished preferment, but he chose to remain at his beloved S Albans. Indeed, towards the end, as his health declined, he began to dread the possibility of having to retire; thankfully God took him before this became necessary, and he passed out of this world, as he had lived, quietly and without fuss.

Owing to a somewhat excessive shyness Lawrence Harding was not easy to get to know intimately, yet, somewhat paradoxically, he immediately inspired confidence which quickly grew to deep affection not only among his own people but also among an ever-increasing number of priests, including the three Bishops under whom he served, and lay people throughout the diocese of Birmingham and beyond. His counsel and advice were sought after and respected not only in diocesan affairs but also in the Church Union, the Ecumenical Society of the Blessed Virgin Mary and at Walsingham.

During the Second World War, Walsingham was in a "restricted area" and few were able to travel there to make the pilgrimage. In order to keep the devotion alive and stimulate interest and support some of us based in London decided to set up an ad hoc committee and enlist the services mainly of the younger clergy. Lawrence's name was suggested as one who from boyhood had had a devotion to the Shrine. He gladly accepted and soon proved himself a most valued and keen member of what became known as the London Committee for Walsingham. His enthusiasm and support in those early days never waned and he was an ardent devotee of the Shrine and all that it stood for until his death. I don't think he ever missed the National Pilgrimage and he came also on many other occasions, public and private. He came because he loved Our Lady and lived the Incarnation and it was appropriate and right that he should be one of the first group of Priest-Clerks admitted to the Order of Our Lady of Walsingham.

All that he stood for and achieved stemmed from his clear and unequivocal sense of the priesthood and the discipline of the priestly life, which made the deepest impression on all who knew him, either as parish priest, as confessor or counsellor or as a personal friend.

Although he was delighted when Bishop Brown appointed him an honorary canon of Birmingham (and quickly went out and ordered all the appropriate vesture for this office!) he was above all content and determined to be no more than "the servant of servants of God", whoever they might be.

J. L. Oldland

Laurence King

died 9 December 1981

Laurence King, O.B.E., F.R.I.B.A., F.S.A., Lay Clerk of the Shrine of Our Lady of Walsingham and Trustee of the Guild of All Souls died on 9th December 1981 and his Funeral Requiem Mass took place at the Church of S. Thomas, Brentwood, Essex. He was aged seventy-four. The Lord Bishop of Chelmsford presided at the Requiem. Bishop Ambrose Weekes preached the Panegyric. The Church was full for the Mass which was attended by Laurence's sister, Refna, his business associates, clergy and religious, representatives of the Guilds and Societies with which he was closely connected, and many other friends.

In his address Bishop Ambrose Weekes spoke of Laurence King's deep spirituality and suggested that his life reflected the divine attributes of God, his Beauty, Truth, Goodness and Love; he spoke of the dedication of Laurence's skills as architect and artist to the Glory of God and to the promotion through his work of Catholic worship centred round the altar and the Mass.

In 1923 Laurence went with his parents and sister to spend Easter at Ventnor and went to S. Alban's, Ventnor to the Service of Tenebrae. He was most aroused by the beauty of the service and from that day on he became interested in the beauty of Catholic worship.

Laurence's first visit to Walsingham was in 1930 before the Holy House was opened, and apart from the War years he visited the Shrine every year. He was very pleased to have been made a Lay Clerk of the Shrine.

Laurence had a great devotion to Our Lady, particularly under her title of Walsingham. There are numerous Shrines of Our Lady designed by him throughout England It gave him particular pleasure to design the Shrine of Our Lady of Walsingham at S. Augustine's Highgate. Laurence built two new churches dedicated to Our Lady, as well as rebuilding S. Mary-le-Bow after bomb damage and Walsingham Parish Church after the disastrous fire.

He was also the architect of the All Souls Chapel in the grounds of the Shrine.

Margaret O'Ferrall

died December 1980

Meg O'Ferrall was known to many pilgrims to the Shrine during the last twenty years. She had recently returned from Devon where she had been living for a brief period. Her funeral service at the little thatched church of Heckingham had a real sense of home-coming. First because she had been brought up in that lovely part of Norfolk where her father had been Rector. Secondly because Meg's life had so clearly been a preparation for the home-call to her heavenly Father.

From about 1930 and right through the War years she worked in London for Dr Barnardo's Homes. Later she had a gift-shop in Norwich which became the haunt of many of the literary and artistic people of the area. Later still, after a brief spell in Blakeney, she came to live in a flat at the Old Vicarage at Walsingham and joined that band of devout women who by their prayer-life and simple acts of service sustain so marvellously the intercessory work of the Shrine.

But Meg was no "pious mouse"; life was fun in her presence. She loved nature (her tiny flat was always filled with flowers); she loved books and good conversation (and used to drive us mad by finishing the *Times* Crossword first every day!); she enjoyed music and parties and painting. And it was all a reflection of her life of faith.

Michael Smith, Priest

died 22 April 1977

It is difficult to find words that "explain" Father Michael. He was known to nearly all those who have made the pilgrimage to Walsingham since he became Vicar of South Creake in 1944: and each one of us will have a different picture we cherish of the Father Smith that we knew.

Never did he miss the great procession in honour of Our Lady on Saturday evening in the pilgrimage season. He swept into the Sacristy, gave a cheery greeting to all assembled and then peered around to find individuals to whom he could be rude (always charitably, of course). He would go into church and pray with his serene, loving attention which he always displayed throughout the proceedings. Afterwards he held court at the pub and this was a real "feature" of the pilgrimage for many who appreciated and looked forward to it.

He came to the Shrine to hear Confessions on Tuesdays throughout the year and he dined with the Shrine clergy and guests each week. The stories he told were hilarious and impossible to relate without his inimitable turn of phrase and expression: and he was easily persuaded to tell a tale to raise spirits, frequently against himself—as when he once searched Fakenham for his car, having forgotten where he had parked it or its colour or number and had to call the police station for help.

But it wasn't only his hilarity that came through on these informal evenings. His knowledge on all sorts of subjects was deep and well thought out. He loved history and invariably had an unusual and fascinating theory about how people ticked in the various epochs of our national life. He adored the countryside and the world of nature: and the ever-changing seasons and moods of his beloved Norfolk were an abiding delight to him.

It was, however, in his lovely church at South Creake that one found the real Michael Smith. Going there to Confession on Easter Even this year was a wonderful experience. The weather was delightful, warm and sunny: and the church looked perfect. Sam, the dog, gambolled around his master, who was pushing a wheelbarrow full of exquisite blooms to decorate the building for the greatest of Festivals. Quietly the parish priest left his chores, pacified Sam, and we all prayed in that blissful spot—all the priestly experience of a life-time seemed to be contained in his advice and one came away feeling important in the eyes and love of God once more through the gentle ministrations of his holy priest. That is the Michael Smith I would like to leave with God.

David Baker

Leonard Arthur Whitmore

Carilloner 1954–1982
Shrine Beadle 1957–1982
Lay Clerk of the Shrine 1959–
1985

died 25 April 1985

Leonard Arthur Whitmore—Len to his friends—was born in Leicester on 17 September, 1913 and educated at Wiggeston Grammar School, Leicester. He grew up in the reign of George V in the aftermath of the first World War, when Europe was trying to rehabilitate itself following four years of slaughter which had destroyed a whole generation.

During the 1939–45 conflict Len was employed on reconditioning engines for army vehicles in what was regarded as a reserved occupation. Subsequently he built up a thriving motor garage business in Gotham Street, Leicester. But Len was never happy running a big concern and as the business prospered and staff problems increased, he looked round for something smaller. His association with Walsingham seems to have begun about

this time, and it suited his plans to obtain premises near the Shrine. And so Len took on his most unlikely role—that of a proprietor of a grocery shop at Briston, a small village about eight miles from Walsingham.

With the business again expanding it was time to move on and to Walsingham. Len disengaged himself from Briston and developed an earlier interest in electrical engineering. Thus began perhaps the most satisfying period of Len's life. He had for some time attended services at St Mary's, Walsingham and the Shrine, and this association was now to become more formal. The Shrine bells had been silent since the death of William Frary, but Len as the new carilloner played them every week until about two years before he died. When the Archbishop of Canterbury visited Walsingham for the 1980 National Pilgrimage, it was as Shrine Beadle that Len headed the procession round the village. For years Len did duty at the Shrine as M.C. for the Saturday night processions. He served on St Mary's P.C.C. and subsequently became a church warden. He was also a parish councillor.

Len was a deeply committed Christian and was never happier than when he could give this some practical expression. Thus for years his devoted work as Shrine electrician. He was always ready to help others—often beyond the call of duty. In fact emergencies seemed to be his speciality! His charitable work on behalf of St Hilary's Children's Home was something too that could be undertaken with tangible results. In all his endeavours Len was supported with great loyalty and generosity of spirit by his wife Rene. Any success he had was hers too.

Retirement was never seriously contemplated and he found it difficult to accept the limitations imposed by increasing ill-health. Having put his affairs in order and handed over the business reins to his son Philip, Len died peacefully in Aylsham hospital.

Stanley Smith

115

The Society of Our Lady of Walsingham

This, the oldest of the organisations connected with Walsingham, grew out of a local guild formed by Father Hope Patten. It was founded in 1925. Originally its members were invested with a blue scapular. In the Summer 1931 number of Our Lady's Mirror, *Father Hope Patten asked those who "no longer had any interest or devotion" to Walsingham to return their scapulars "as we want this confraternity to be a living reality and a zealous body, and would infinitely rather have just a hundred keen members than a thousand indifferent confrères".*

Alice Mary England

died 15 May 1945

Many pilgrims will remember Miss England. She has been the greatest standby both in the parish and the revival of the devotion to O.L.W. for the past twenty-four years. When the Parish Priest came to Walsingham in 1921 she was the first to come to his support and welcome the changes which were then and onward made. She joined the Society of Mary (then the League), and was a most devoted Sister of the Society of our Lady of Walsingham, and at her wish she was buried in the large blue veil and insignia of this latter Society. Her love for the Mother of God was very real and deep. She was one of those placid, calm and ever-dependable people, one from whom you never heard an unkind word or criticism of others. Many will miss her secret but constant charity and help, for which she denied herself for years.

William Frary

died 15 August 1953

Mr. William Frary was known to so many pilgrims and visitors to the Shrine just by his Christian name, for he was everyone's friend, and all lovers of Walsingham were his friends.

For over thirty years he had been a regular server and M.C. at the Parish Church of S. Mary; one of the first members of the S.O.L.W., and from the time of the rebuilding of the Holy House he had been Beadle, Gardener and Carillonneur.

William was always at hand and ready for any call at any time, for time did not matter to him so long as he was doing "a job" for the Shrine or anything or anyone connected with it.

He was a devoted and loyal worker, and also a personal and valued friend to so many.

Since he was a young man of seventeen he had been most regular in his personal religion, and a real defender of the Faith in our village. Many souls have been helped over difficult stiles by him, and he will be long remembered and loved.

William died, as he wished, on Our Lady's Assumption.

A.H.P.

The Priest Associates were started in connection with the Society in 1927. One of the first members was a previous vicar of Walsingham, George Ratcliffe Woodward. They numbered 125 in the spring of 1932.

Alexander Cuthbert Lawson, Priest
died 17 May 1966

Recently there died suddenly a Priest Associate who was probably known to very few others, but who had a great influence upon Walsingham in the early days. Alexander Lawson who in his youth lived with Fr. Roger Wodehouse in Oxford, was enormously knowledgeable about Shrines of Our Lady on the Continent and was amongst the first pilgrims to the restored Shrine at Walsingham. It was he who persuaded Fr. Hope Patten to dress the image according to mediaeval custom, and he provided the Silver Crown which is known today as the Oxford Crown. He was a priest of great integrity and never feared to make himself unpopular by speaking his mind and demonstrating to other people their wrong-headedness. He was Vicar of St. Ives, Hunts, for sixteen years 1946–62 until ill-health compelled him to retire. He had not been much to Walsingham in recent years, but he made a pilgrimage on the Sunday before he died, which was an appropriate end to the life of one who had a great devotion to Our Lady and had done much to forward her honour in this Country.

His books and albums of postcards form the nucleus of the Shrine's Marian Library.

The Sisters

One of Fr. Hope Patten's great hopes when he restored the Shrine of Our Lady of Walsingham was that there would be a Religious House here. At first some Sisters came from Horbury and lived in the Vicarage cottage until the Hospice was opened. Later, when that Community divided, the Sisters at Walsingham came from the house which was founded at Laleham. All these original Sisters who worked at Walsingham are remembered with great affection and gratitude by the villagers and older pilgrims.

During the War there was an attempt to found a Community of Our Lady of Walsingham, but in spite of gallant efforts it was not successful and it seemed that the Shrine would be left without Sisters.

The Society of St Margaret

The connection with Walsingham began in 1947 when, in the middle of a record-breaking winter, Fr Hope Patten made the journey to S Saviour's Priory at the suggestion of the Guardians to ask Mother Cicely for help in running the Pilgrim Hospice and the Shrine. History relates that, due to the post-war rigours and the atrocious weather, Father Patten made at least part of the journey on a goods train. Mother Cicely's response was immediate and firm— there was no way that she was going to spare any of her sisters; they were all much too involved in their work in the local parishes. Not untypically, Father Patten insisted: Mother Cicely phoned the Chaplain, Father Mather, and asked his advice: Father Mather also insisted that

L to r: *Novice Shirley, S. Jean, S. Mary Kathleen, S. Elizabeth, S. Ann, S. Wendy, S. Clare, Mother Julian, S. Olive, S. Angela. S. Angela was sacristan to the shrine for over 40 years. S. Julian cooked for the Hospice for 25 years and was sacristan at the parish church.*

some sisters should be sent; so Mother Cicely agreed. On April 16th, 1947, Sister Margaret, Sister Angela and Sister Julian arrived in Walsingham, with some snow still on the ground. Because of the War, the whole of the "set up" in Walsingham had become, at least from the inside, somewhat run-down: there had been hardly any pilgrims during the war because of the Shrine being in the middle of a Restricted Area.

Work started immediately for the sisters, with one or two hiccups. On their first morning they were due at the Parish Church for Mass at 7.30 a.m., but they became lost on their way and were nearly in Houghton S Giles before Sister Julian noticed the Church steeple receding in the distance behind them.

From 1947 until 1955 the sisters lived in the Hospice, at the "All Souls' Chapel" end. In 1955, almost to mark the centenary of the founding of the Society, a new convent was built, and Sister Margaret became the first Reverend Mother of the new affiliated house. For the first year their chapel was a wooden hut—Mother Margaret had insisted upon a stone altar for the chapel, and so the altar was constructed first and the wooden structure was built over the top of it. Then, due to the generosity of an Associate's bequest, the present brick building was erected in 1956.

Mother Margaret Mary S.S.M.
died 18 April 1969

On a foggy morning in April, 1947, Fr. Hope Patten arrived on the doorstep of St. Saviour's Priory, Haggerston, and when he was shown into the Reverend Mother's room he said at once "Mother, I want Sisters for Walsingham". Mother Cecily replied "It is quite impossible!" and then after a pause she added "but we must do it!". An unhappy sequence of events had led up to this request so that it was a mission of some delicacy. The Mother knew that she was giving the Sister-in-charge of the small group she intended to send an assignment which needed great tact and abundant charity. She chose as leader Sister Margaret Mary, who she rightly judged, could deal with the situation in which the Sisters must identify themselves completely with the Shrine and yet preserve a greater measure of independence than those who had worked there before.

There was accommodation in the pilgrim hospice, but it was very cramped and there was little privacy. A tin hut served as a chapel. The Sisters immediately and without fuss took over the running of the temporal side of the pilgrimage work, the organisation of the Sacristy, and threw themselves whole-heartedly into the life of the village.

For Sister Margaret, leaving Haggerston where she had grown up in the religious life was a great wrench. She loved the unattractive and very unhygienic streets around the Priory but she had an overwhelming affection for the people who lived in them. She once confessed that very often at Walsingham when she had been at prayer she would blink her eyes and wonder where she was as she had in her prayer been transported back to the chapel of St. Saviour's Priory. The people in the various East End parishes served by the Community loved her in return and never forgot her. When she returned to end her days at St. Saviour's Priory, almost twenty-five years later, there was great rejoicing in many homes around Haggerston.

At Walsingham she was the Superior and had the very difficult task of arranging the work of her small Community and jealously safeguarding their life of prayer. So often she would take on tasks herself in order that others should not miss their periods of quiet withdrawal from the heavy activity connected with the work of the Shrine.

A mark of the Sisters of St. Saviour's has always been their readiness to take on difficult work, and Mother Margaret, as she became, not only had this characteristic but would even embrace it joyfully. It was no uncommon experience to approach her with what one felt was an unreasonable demand and be completely disarmed by a charming smile and the reply "that will be lovely!" and she meant it, for she had a charity which was able to find deep happiness in the service of others.

This was the secret of her power over the pilgrims and during the years she was at Walsingham she made innumerable friends, and in her little office in the hospice people opened their hearts to her and she was able to exact a pastoral ministry which was invaluable in such a place. Particularly she was kind and sympathetic towards those who were not accustomed to the sort of religion found at the Shrine and so often it was her love and understanding which won them completely.

From her first arrival at Walsingham her ideal had been to find accommodation away from the hospice where the Sisters could enjoy a degree of enclosure which she felt essential for the maintenance of the very active life they were forced to live. It was characteristic of her that she almost literally built an altar and then let the Convent develop around it. In 1955 it was made into an independent house with Sister Margaret Mary as its first Mother. The constitution places a great deal of responsibility in the hands of the Mother and Mother Margaret found that the office, for her, involved a great deal of suffering. When things began to change in the Church she like many other religious, was torn between the traditions of her Community as she had received them, and growing relaxation of ancient disciplines which was taking place everywhere. She was forced to give way over some things, but it was a great agony for her, and to the end of her life, far from desiring relaxation, she was always afraid that she was not giving enough. It was indeed the love of Christ which constrained her.

She always looked frail in health but was in fact enormously tough and could do without sleep and warmth to a remarkable degree. It was hard for her to realize that the new generation had less steel in their make-up than her own contemporaries, but she expected far more from herself than she did from any of her Sisters.

When her health began to fail it presented certain difficulties for those who lived with her because, although in pain and discomfort, she would never mention it and would make light of it if asked. As she approached her 80th year she felt convinced that she should resign her office as Mother which she did gladly and willingly.

In such a small Community it was not easy for an ex-Mother to obliterate her office completely, and so it was decided, at her own request, that she should return to St. Saviour's Priory in 1968. She did not live long but it was a happy time in her old home and there was great rejoicing at her return.

Colin Stephenson

The College of St. Augustine

Father Hope Patten seems to have envisaged the establishment of a college of Augustin-
ians from the start. This extract, written in 1948, shows that he dated its beginning
from the time the newly ordained Derrick Lingwood joined him in the Vicarage. The
College moved into its permanent buildings, though not then completed, during the
Octave of the Assumption 1945.

For fourteen years we have been trying to establish the College, and after all that
time there are only three of us professed: Father Hope Patten, Father Derrick
Lingwood and Brother Peter Harbottle, and at the moment there are two Novices.
Indeed, very few have been to test their vocation, and there have been in all only
three priests and four laymen who have done so in addition to the five of us at
present at S. Augustine's. The seven who have been to test their vocation all found
and proved that they were not called to this life, as of course it is a particular
vocation, and it is obvious that there cannot be a large number of men who are
suitable. "Without doubt the needs of Walsingham and the Shrine make this vocation
in many respects different from an ordinary community and in some ways more
exacting," but the need of men with vocations to give their lives for this particular
calling of prayer and work is very urgent. Priests and laymen are needed who in due
course will be able to carry on the tradition and continue the organisation and
direction of the Shrine and its various ramifications.

The life of the Walsingham College is a modernised form of that lived under the rule
of S. Augustine since the 5th century. Their houses were particularly popular in
England from the 12th to 16th century. The Canons of S. Augustine and other
bodies of men living under that rule were communities between the monastic and the
secular clergy, and in some measure having the characteristics of both. The
Augustinians, while living in community, were much freer than the monks and less
independent than the secular clergy. Their houses were very numerous in this
country. Their members varied much in number, but the majority of these Colleges
(or Communities) had only four or five professed brethren, with the exception of a
few larger houses, consisting of a dozen or fifteen in life vows.
    They were not by any means all priests, and there was little difference made
between the Brothers and those in Sacred Orders, except that the Prior (Provost,
Warden or whatever title was given to the head) was *usually* in major Orders. By
the 15th century, however, the choir members were generally priests, deacons,
sub-deacons and acolytes.
    The habit consisted of a girded gown or cassock, with a rochet or surplice and
cappa. The mozetta replaced the cappa from Easter to All Saints', together with a
tall biretta worn by all indiscriminately. The colour varied, and might be white or
grey, but more usually black. The noviciate lasted for one year, after which life vows
were taken. At Walsingham, a postulancy of at least three months is required,
followed by a noviciate or, as it is called with us, a period of junior membership
lasting for at least two years, after which profession is made in chapter and installation in choir. This profession is made with a life intention, but subject to renewal
every three years. Candidates for ordination are not received, and applicants should
have finished their military service before coming to the College.

A. Hope Patten

Administrator's cottage: top, *Spring, 1944,* bottom, *August, 1945.*

Life in the College of St. Augustine 1946–49

by Leslie Oldroyd (Brother David)

On the 31st March 1946 I made my first visit to Walsingham on a bicycle whilst stationed at RAF Langham awaiting demobilisation. It was a glorious Sunday morning and I fell "hook, line and sinker" for the place. During the next couple of months I got to know Father Hope Patten well and he suggested that I might like to join his community of Augustinian Canons. I simply couldn't wait! So, on the 1st August that year I duly presented myself at the College. The only members were Fr. Hope Patten, Fr. Derrick Lingwood and Br. Peter who were all novices, with Fr. Patten acting as Superior. On 2nd September I was admitted as a postulant and about that time Br. John joined us. We brothers were just back from the war, very keen and extremely "spikey". Walsingham was "magic" and in spite of our travels abroad we had come across nothing like this.

Over the period of the next two years we experimented with the Horarium, and indeed the Divine Office itself in attempts to find something that suited Fr. Patten. I spent hours typing out various versions of the Day Hours but we never found one that really pleased him. Our timetable eventually settled down as follows: Matins and Prime 6.30 a.m.—then we all went to the Parish Church for the 7.30 Mass and took our turns serving—Breakfast at 8.15; Mental Prayer, Terce, Chapter Mass, Sext followed at 9.20;. After this we worked until 12.45 when we made a visit to the Blessed Sacrament. Lunch at 1, during which a book was read. None at 2 and then more work until tea time at 4.30. Evensong at 5.30 followed by Rosary, Intercessions and various other devotions. Dinner at 7. Compline 9.30, after which Greater Silence was observed until after Sext next morning. Life was very full for in addition to work at the Shrine we were active in 3 parishes with children's clubs, catechisms etc.

Fr. Hope Patten was a great disciplinarian—one look from him was enough to let an offender know he had gone too far. An avid reader of spiritual books and lives of the Saints himself, he also supervised our reading with scrupulous care. A great advocate of the Jesus Prayer, he urged everyone to use it. Those who had the privilege of living the Collegiate life with him could not but be aware that he himself was a man of prayer. He had a tremendous sense of humour and of the ridiculous. His great dignity and self-discipline made some people rather afraid of him but he had a very human and sympathetic nature in understanding the problems of others. He was very meticulous—everything started on time, ceremonial had to be perfect and the Sacristy was a place of almost perpetual Silence!

Life in the College was spartan. Those of us who lived in St. Augustine's had to get water from the pump in the quad, and we had no heating in our cells apart from a small one-bar electric fire which had to be used sparingly. The food was good although rationing still existed. In spite of these rather tough conditions we dined in style in the lovely College Refectory being waited on by Fr. Patten's devoted valet George Long.

On Feast days (and there were many) the boys from the Children's Home came to serve at Chapter Mass with the pupils of the Sanctuary School singing in the loft. Ceremonial was carried out under the careful eye of William Frary the beadle who was a superb M.C. and could do just about anything required of him.

We were all devoted to the children at the Home and on Sunday nights when everything was over it was our custom to go up to St. Hilary's and spend a couple of hours to relax with the children, Fr. Patten usually being the life and soul of the

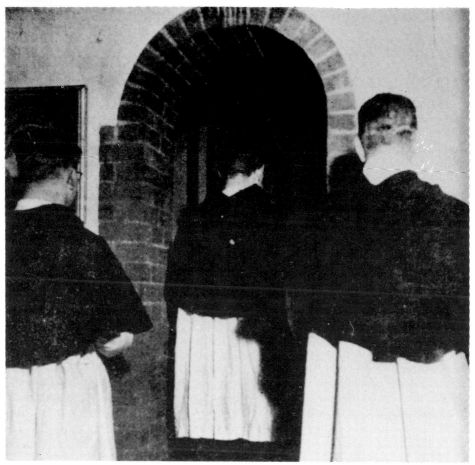

party. The brothers were not normally allowed to socialise in the parish but occasionally Fr. Patten, who admired and respected Enid Chadwick and appreciated her great work for the Shrine, would allow the brothers to spend a musical evening in her cottage. Br. Anthony played the piano, Miss Chadwick the violin and the rest of us warbled ballads with gusto. Although women were strictly forbidden in the College precincts Father was always concerned for Miss Chadwick's welfare and insisted that a tea tray was sent to her studio every afternoon.

Fr. Patten's ideal of the priesthood was of the highest order. This he instilled into Fr. Lingwood, who himself was a very remarkable man. Although never very enthusiastic about being an Augustinian he rarely missed Office in spite of being the busiest man in the place. Fr. Derrick was everywhere!—Shrine Office, Council meetings, doing great work at St. Peter's and St. Giles; much loved by the parishioners but still playing his part in the community life. He, like Fr. Patten, never forgot that he was first and foremost a priest.

We had crisis after crisis of great magnitude. Satan tried every trick in the book but Fr. Patten battled on. The Community of Our Lady of Walsingham—a small order of Sisters which had been founded to serve the Shrine—began to founder and eventually closed. Fr. Patten—as only he could—managed to beg some Sisters from

Haggerston who responded magnificently. The matron at the Home resigned and again Father managed to get the ideal ladies—"Barty and Miss Will" to save the day. Trouble at the Sanctuary School—a new headmaster and staff needed Father got them. But all these things were a great strain on him. Even those days there were pious ladies of means who managed to buy property and settle here to "assist" at the Shrine. They were a formidable gathering, often at "daggers drawn" with each other but Fr. Patten was able to control them and indeed make great use of them. Little wonder that he would work himself to a standstill and had to go away to recuperate. It was usually one of my duties to accompany him on these rest cures. He was an agreeable and fascinating companion, and once away from his work he would relax and was not difficult to look after. I regret that I did not keep a diary or write down the many interesting things he told me about his life and work.

It was generally agreed in the College that Father was psychic and indeed his ghost stories were spine-chilling, many of which he claimed to be true. Certainly we had some weird experiences in St Augustine's. One night Brother Anthony was working quietly in his cell when his door suddenly opened wide—there was no one about. Anthony, who was sceptical about ghosts, closed the door carefully only for it to open again a moment later. At the same moment a large candle before the statue of St Anthony broke into two (wick and all) and flew on to the bed. That did it! Anthony called Brother John and together scringing and trembling they knocked up Father Patten who came nonchalantly with a bucket of holy water and blessed the room. On another occasion Brother John who was on "bell duty" went to ring the bell for Compline. The Shrine was pitch dark apart from the lamp flickering before the tabernacle. As John genuflected his foot touched something which he imagined to be a kneeling-mat. He bent down to move the mat but to his horror it moved and he gave a great shriek and fled. In fact he grabbed the foot of Sister Mary Phillida* who was almost invisible in the darkness. This revered recluse was saying her prayers before the Blessed Sacrament and we never found out what she thought about the incident!

One night at Compline we were all startled to hear a strange muffled knocking in the region of the organ loft. "Ghosts", whispered Father Patten to Brother David, who immediately pulled from his pocket a huge rosary and crossed himself at speed. This reduced the Community to hysterics and Compline was suspended whilst Father Patten went to investigate. The ghost turned out to be Sister Grizel hammering a set of Stations of the Cross on the wall of the Sisters' Chapel which at that time was behind the organ loft! This delightful Sister was a great do-it-yourselfer and cleverly repaired a broken-down seat which was on the lawn in front of the nuns' part of the Hospice. She then painted the seat and the Sisters were invited to admire it and sit upon it, which they did. Unfortunately the paint was still wet and the Sisters were greatly disturbed to have green stripes across their bottoms! On another occasion Sister Grizel dropped a jug into the holy well (which was not at that time so deep). Instead of getting a rake which would have easily retrieved the jug the dear Sister, after making sure no one was about, removed her shoes and stockings, rolled up her habit and went down the well on a ladder to get her jug. Alas, one of the brothers appeared as she came out and the story gave Father Patten and the College much pleasure.

A much loved member of the College was Nicholas the College cat. He had the charming habit of allowing ladies to stroke him and gush over him for he was a magnificent cat. When they turned away he would rive his great claws down their legs and more than one shattered gimmer had to be assisted to the Hospice for first

* Sister Mary Phillida lived as a recluse in the grounds of the Shrine from 1934 until her death in 1985.

125

aid. Our cook, Mary Harrison, in spite of hers being the hand that fed Nicholas, suffered much from him. Many a dark night when Mary was taking the kitchen keys to Father Derrick's cottage a piercing scream would be heard in the quad where Nicholas would be lurking by the pump in order to attack Mary's legs. William, who lived next door to the College, had a ginger cat who was Nicholas' deadliest enemy. One evening Ginger trespassed into the College garden only to be hotly pursued by Nicholas—both ending up in William's hen-run where a terrible fight ensued with hens squawking and flying about in terror and panic.

Of the many guests we entertained one or two remain vividly in one's mind. Sir William Milner was a frequent visitor being a great personal friend of Father Patten. Sir William was a giant of a man—gentle, devout and courteous. Invariably late for meals it was thought simpler to send him a breakfast tray to his bed. More than once, hampered by his size, Sir William upset the whole tray over the bed. Poor George who had to clear it up was extraordinarily patient about this. Father Raymond Raynes CR was a regular and interesting guest. Dinner—of which he partook frugally—dragged on owing to his illuminating and witty conversation. Bishop O'Rorke intrigued Father Patten by taking Carter's Little Liver Pills after meals and tempted Father Patten to try them. Dear old Father Fynes-Clinton, full of heraldry, South India and many interesting topics kept us entertained night after night. To see him taking his pilgrimage of doting old ladies round the Shrine booming "Orate" was a treat indeed. Relations between the RC Shrine and ours were not cordial in those days and on the occasion of one great Roman pilgrimage—Cardinal and all—we brothers invited Father Patten and Father Fynes to come over and listen to the news on our radio. A very posh voice began to describe the Roman Pilgrimage and referred to the Vicar of Walsingham as "the Protestant Minister Mr. Patten". Two very indignant and outraged priests could hardly believe their ears. Choking with fury Father Fynes was all for complaining to the BBC. We then produced the "news reader"—Brother Peter who had been hiding in the loft with a microphone attached to the radio set. Fortunately for us the two fathers were highly amused and took it in good part. Father Fynes never forgot it and chuckled a great deal. Guardians—carefully chosen by Father came to Chapter meetings—and did as they were told! Of course, no Guardian of those days would ever dream of telling the Administrator how to run the Shrine!!

We ourselves had our own Chapter Meetings. These took place in our little Chapter House which had been made in an old tiny kitchen next to the library. Every Monday after None we would go in procession to the Chapter House where we confessed our breaches of the Rule. I still have notes of some of these "faults" mainly breaches of the Silence. We then discussed any business requiring attention. One day Father Patten said that he felt he should now be addressed as Father Prior as he and Father Derrick and Brother Peter were by now professed. Most of us felt this to be rather premature so there was a long silence. Father looked stoney. Then he said "So you propose this, Brother David?" "Well, I suppose so", I said, "And you second it, Brother John?" "Very well, Father," "Right, that's settled" beamed Father Patten and closed the meeting. One memorable Chapter Meeting will never be forgotten. It happened that the lavatory in the Undercroft was blocked and Ivan Frary and his assistant were trying to locate the blockage. Between the Shrine Church and the College was a wicker gate and on the College side of the gate was a manhole inspection cover (it is still there). The cover had been removed by Ivan and as we processed round the corner we were confronted by the hole—the juniors in the lead side-stepped it but poor Father Derrick stepped into the revolting mess, falling back into Father Patten's arms, biretta and glasses askew whilst Father cried, "Oh, Derrick, Derrick!" Father Derrick retreated to his cottage to get cleaned up

The College refectory.

and the procession continued and the Chapter was held. We brothers were choking
with suppressed laughter and joy whilst Father Patten with a face like thunder
conducted the meeting. Towards the end Father Derrick returned and announced
that the cause of the blockage was half a pair of RAF underpants with the name
OLDROYD on them! A poem in memory of this occasion was later written much to
the disapproval of Father Patten.

After nearly 4 years I moved on to test my vocation in more established communities but nothing was ever like Walsingham. It is impossible to assess how much I

127

Sketch by Enid Chadwick of the ruined cottages fronting Knight's Street which are now incorporated into the College.

owe to Father Patten. Great romantic and dreamer that he was, with something of a touch of Aelred Carlyle in his make up, he had the driving force and personality to get his own way to the point of being ruthless occasionally, but he was also a man of great sympathy and understanding of the problems of others and would spend hours in the Confessional giving wise counsel when it was needed. The Congregation of S Augustine was his own personal ambition; appeals for vocations are to be found in issue after issue of *Our Lady's Mirror* but it never really flourished. His great work of restoring the Shrine stands firm but his Community, alas, was not to be.

Our Lady Through Anglican Eyes

"Yes, we will love thee, Mother dear."

An Address in the Pilgrimage Church on 6 July 1956, by the Rev. S. John Forrest.

THERE is a striking hymn in honour of Our Lady beginning with the words, "Shall we not love thee, Mother dear." It will serve us very well as a kind of text upon which to hang our meditations this evening.

Let us take it verse by verse:-

> "Shall we not love thee, Mother dear,
> Whom Jesus loves so well;
> And to his glory year by year,
> Thy joy and honour tell?"

To begin with, let us note three things:-

First, we are speaking to a Person; a real, living being. It is not just a rhetorical or poetical question, for the whole hymn (except the last verse), is addressed to the blessed Mother of Christ, who is not a dead character of past history, not a figure of fiction, but alive for evermore with her Son in heaven.

Secondly, we address her as "Mother dear." She is not a foster-mother but our own true mother; for we are members of Christ, limbs of His Body, born into the Church by baptism. And so she who was the mother of his physical body is also mother of his mystical body, the Church, and therefore is mother of all Christian people, whether we realise it or no.

Thirdly, we note that we are to tell, year by year, the joy and honour of Blessed Mary; not for her own sake alone, but for the glory of our Lord Jesus Christ:

> "And to His glory, year by year.
> Thy Joy and honour tell."

There are many people who fear that if we honour Mary we shall somehow defraud Jesus. Yet, surely a little reflection ought to show us that this is not really true. It cannot be pleasing to our Lord that we should treat his Mother with irreverence. What do you think of people who are rude to your mother? When friends were kind to my mother in her last hours on earth, and so many were, I felt a deep sense of gratitude towards them. So too, our divine Lord who so loved his Mother, must surely appreciate any love and honour that we may show to her for his sake. One thing is quite certain: if we could devote our whole life to Mary, we could not love her more than Jesus did, for his love was perfect and absolute.

We will take the next two verses of the hymn together:

> "Bound with the curse of sin and shame,
> We helpless sinners lay,
> Until in tender love he came,
> To bear the curse away.
>
> And thee he chose from whom to take
> True flesh his flesh to be;
> In it to suffer for our sake.
> By it to make us free."

There in two simple verses you have the whole gospel story.

Man, bound by sin, crying out for redemption, "mourning and weeping in this vale of tears," until God decreed to send the Redeemer to offer his perfect sacrifice, oblation and satisfaction for the sins of mankind, upon the cross.

129

And of all women upon the earth, He chose Mary of Nazareth to be his Mother. There had been plenty of good women before her time: Sarah, Rachel, Judith, Esther, Ruth the Moabitess; and there have been many since: St. Monica, St. Catherine of Siena, St. Clare, St. Elizabeth of Hungary, the two St. Teresas; or great women like Florence Nightingale, Mary Slessor of Calabar, Mary Sumner, Josephine Butler, and many more. *But none of these was good enough.* God could see them all in his simultaneous vision, for past, present and future are all eternally present to Him. No; He could only focus his divine purpose on the greatest of all women, the finest blossom of womanhood that this world has ever seen: Mary the maid of the village of Nazareth in Galilee.

> "And thee he chose of whom to take
> True flesh his flesh to be."

So for ever now, this Maiden is related to God in an absolutely different way from any other human creature, for she is a blood-relation of God incarnate: she gave him her flesh and her blood that He might have a perfect human nature wherein to redeem mankind.

We continue with our hymn:

> "Thy Babe He lay upon thy breast,
> To thee he cried for food,
> Thy gentle nursing soothed to rest
> The incarnate Son of God."

Blessed Mary did not fail in her vocation. Not only was she the honoured Mother of God, not only was she privileged above all women, but she was, above all, the handmaid of the Lord, the bond-slave of the Lord: and, as her own Son later testified, she heard the word of God and kept it. That was her greatest "joy and honour", and this we pledge ourselves to proclaim to the glory of her dear Son.

The worship that we give to Jesus and the honour that we accord to Mary are of quite a different kind. Jesus is God and we worship Him with the supreme adoration that would be idolatry if given to any merely human being, even to the purest of creatures. But there is another kind of honour, the lesser honour of which St. Paul speaks when he says: "Render honour to whom honour is due." And to whom is it due more superlatively than to our Blessed Lady?

> "O wondrous depth of grace divine,
> That He should bend so low,
> And Mary O what joy 'twas thine,
> In his dear love to know."

You and I tend to take this "wondrous depth of grace divine" in so matter-of-fact a way! And yet it is so tremendous, so inconceivable. Can we imagine the infinite gulf that separates God and man, eternity and time: and can we imagine a bridge across that gulf linking up the two? Jesus Christ is that Bridge, spanning the chasm; and this Bridge rests upon two piers which support it at either side. At the Heavenly end it rests upon the Most Holy Trinity, at the earthly end upon the Blessed Virgin Mary. Take away either of the piers and the Bridge collapses. Deny that Jesus is indeed the Second Person of the Godhead and you make nonsense of the gospel itself; you turn it into a tragedy, a grim story of a Hero who lost his life trying to serve God. Deny, on the other hand, that Mary is the ever-virgin Mother of God and you, ipso facto, deny the reality of our redemption. For it is essential that we believe her to be the doorway through which he entered into this world, and from whom he took *true flesh* his flesh to be; that she held in her arms, suckled and nursed a Baby who was truly God and perfectly human also.

130

"Joy to be Mother of the Lord,
And thine the truer bliss,
In every thought and deed and word,
To be for ever his.

And as He loves thee Mother dear,
We too will love thee well;
And to His glory year by year,
Thy joy and honour tell."

During the last century, as we well know, there has been a great revival of devotion in honour of the Mother of Christ. At first it met with great prejudice, but thanks to the work of the Catholic movement it is gradually melting away. When I was curate of Oakham stories were being told of a noble peer who beckoned to a churchwarden and asked him, "Jones, that figure in the window over the Lord's table, in the Trinity chapel. Is that supposed to be the Virgin?"

"Yes, my Lord," was the reply. At which the nobleman seized his hat and left the church for ever.

How different things are to-day you can see for yourself by attending a diocesan Mothers' Union Festival and counting the very many gorgeous banners bearing the image of Our Lady.

The M.U. has done great work in wearing away ignorant prejudice about Our Lady, and we must in no way despise this contribution to Marian devotion even if it doesn't succeed in reaching the "Walsingham standard."

Quite the most phenomenal movement in our Church has been the wonderful revival of this Walsingham pilgrimage. As long as Walsingham exists, Our Lady will never be absolutely ignored or forgotten in the Church of England. She who is the Ark of the New Covenant is enthroned here. In ancient times that golden chest, the Ark, was the symbol of the abiding presence of God with his people. In that Ark were the stone tables containing the Commandments, the rod of Aaron (token of the true priesthood), and the pot of manna, the bread from heaven. In Mary, Ark of the New Covenant, there abode Christ the final Lawgiver, the great High Priest, and the Living Bread. She opened up her Treasure to the world and gave Him to mankind. So that every good gift and every perfect gift brought to us by the Incarnation comes to us through Mary. That is just undeniable fact.

"Thou wast the gate of Heaven's high Lord,
The door through which the light has poured;
Christians rejoice for through a maid
To all mankind is life conveyed."

Did God use her in that way once long ago and then discard her for evermore? Is that God's way?

Certainly not! "Thou hast been faithful over a few things, I will make thee ruler over many things." Every Christian who does his job well is to have vastly increased responsibilities in the life to come.

What then of our Blessed Lady? If that mighty treasury of blessings which we call the Incarnation came through her in the first instance, has she any lesser function now in the Heavens?

No, I firmly believe that still today she is intimately associated, by her powers of intercession, with every good gift and every perfect gift that comes from the Most Holy Trinity.

Whether people like it or not, whether they love Mary or not, she loves every one of us; she is praying for all, she is working with her divine Son in the unseen spheres to fashion each one of us into His likeness. One day those who have denied her love, or blasphemed her holy name, will awaken to the fact that they have spurned the gracious fondling of their most lovely Mother. And how terrible will their remorse then be!

God has given to his Mother great privileges and a mighty power of intercession. No one need fear that she will misuse her gifts or her power. She will not attempt to divert us from God; she will not scheme to attract us to the worship of anything less than the Most Holy Trinity: she will not jealously capture our devotion and hug it to her own self; she will not eclipse or obscure the streaming light of the divine Christ; she will do nothing to detract from His supreme godhead or his perfect manhood. Her one and only wish is to remain the handmaid of the Lord, and that all things shall be according to his word. Her one desire for us is that we should be like her, and thereby like him, in hearing the word of God and keeping it, her one command to men is: "Whatsoever he saith unto you, do it."

There she sits enthroned at his right hand; a glorious suppliant Queen beside her Lord and King. Yet what a suppliant! So near to God, so understanding of his mind, so ready to co-operate with His will. Remember that the Christian must see the universe as a great fellowship of co-workers: all working together with God. It has pleased Him to delegate much of his work; some to the holy angels, some to the saints, and some even to us sinners here below. And in our devotional life the perspective will be distorted (to say the least) if we do not give Our Lady thousand times ten thousand and thousands of thousands, it is only when we realise that upon the King's right hand stands the Queen in vesture of gold, and that around them is the court of Heaven numbering ten thousand times ten thousand and thousands of thousands, it is only when we make contact with that glorious array that our minds are really opened to the full grandeur of God, who reigns not as a solitary tyrant in lonely state, but as the loving Parent of that most wonderful of families, from which every family on earth is named—the family of the Holy Catholic Church which is also the Communion of Saints.

> "Yes we will love thee Mother dear,
> Whom Jesus loves so well."

Bishop Mervyn Stockwood, then Bishop of Southwark, was the first English diocesan bishop to preach at the restored Shrine, at the National Pilgrimage, 7 June 1965. He was later made an honorary Guardian. On another occasion, he said 'No matter how we may explain Walsingham, we cannot explain it away. And I am one of the thousands to whom it has been a Jacob's ladder, a point of meeting between heaven and earth.'

The Spirit of God moved upon the face of the waters.   Genesis 1, v.2

The Holy Spirit will come upon you, the power of the Most High will overshadow you.   Luke 1, v.35

Before their eyes appeared tongues like flame which separated off and settled above the heads of each one of them and they were all filled with the Holy Spirit. Acts 2, v.3

Waste, void, darkness and the Spirit of God moved on the face of the waters and God said "Let there be light" and there was light. Thus at the beginning of history we see God's design for his creation. Darkness gives place to light, formlessness to form, unconsciousness to consciousness, and then Man. Think of it as a peak on a mountain range. There it is, the creation, like the Matterhorn in the Alps superb in its glory. Stand on the top, survey the scene, and in the distance see two more peaks.

The first the Incarnation: the Spirit again moves—the Annunciation to the Virgin Mary. "The Holy Spirit will come upon you, the power of the Most High will overshadow you." God's second creative act.

The other peak is Pentecost. The light penetrates, disrupts, energises, and the divine community the Catholic church, the Christian community is born. Creation, Incarnation, the Church three prongs of the fork with which God digs his universe to produce the harvest, the Kingdom of God.

Walsingham pin-points these events, for in honouring Our Lady we acknowledge the niche which is uniquely hers in the unfolding of the divine plan. She is involved in each of the movements of the Spirit—she is a child of the first creation, an instrument in the second, and a participant in the third. No wonder we who are the inheritors of these events come here today to salute her: "Hail,

Mary, full of grace, the Lord is with thee, Blessed art thou among women and blessed is the fruit of thy womb, Jesus, Holy Mary, Mother of God, pray for us sinners now and at the hour of our death."

We must however be careful not to honour her in isolation but always within the context of the plan in which she and we are part. She brought to birth the Christ, and the Church is bringing to birth the reign of the Christ. Mary said, "Behold the handmaid of the Lord, be it unto me according to thy word" The Church says, "Thy Kingdom come, thy will be done on earth as it is in heaven".

What does that mean for us who because of our baptisms are commissioned to be agents of God's Kingdom and God's Will? Let's make no mistake about it—just as God willed to use Mary to accomplish his immediate purpose, so he wills to use us to accomplish his present purpose—and his purpose is nothing less than to establish his sovereignty in all departments of life. To understand what is involved we need to go no further than the Magnificat. "When Christ is King he scatters the proud in the imagination of their hearts—that is *MORAL* change. When Christ is King he puts down the mighty and exalts the humble—that is *SOCIAL* change. When Christ is King he fills the hungry with good things and sends the rich empty away—that is *ECONOMIC* change. It is one thing to sing the

Magnificat to Stanford in B, another to take the words of Our Lady seriously and let her spell out a practical programme of change. I have no doubt that if the Church is to influence contemporary society we must move along these three lines of change, moral, social and economic.

Moral change: not a book of rules, not a list of commandments, but a heart submitted to God—"behold the hand-maid of the Lord be it unto me according to thy word," said Mary. "My heart is restless until it rests in thee," said one of the great Fathers of the Church.

It comes to the same thing, true discipleship begins when the Spirit of God moves on the water and in the darkness of men's sinful hearts; when the light of the redeeming Christ penetrates, when we acknowledge him as Saviour and Lord. Our forefathers talked of conversion and entire consecration—let us restore these words to our vocabulary. In the last resort only one thing matters—we must walk in the presence of God and like St. Paul say of our Lord Jesus, "Whose I am and whom I serve".

I hope you will not think it inappropriate if I give a personal testimony. When it was decided I should be Bishop of Southwark I made a private pilgrimage to this place. It was on the eve of the announcement in the Press. It was a cold and misty November day, the Shrine was deserted. You will not expect me to reveal what passed through my mind as I knelt here alone. Suffice it to say that I realised perhaps more clearly than I had realised it before that Our Lady symbolised two things: devotion to our Lord and charity towards others. And I knew that I should be judged, as indeed every Christian will be judged, by those two things—no matter what one's antecedents may be, one's churchmanship or the "dotted line" on which one writes one's signature, the two things which come above all else are our devotion to our Lord and charity towards each other. Without these our

Christian profession is null and void.

Secondly, Social change: If you were a student at a university writing a thesis on the religions of the world you would devote some chapters to the impact made by these religions on social development, their influence on justice, welfare, communal living, education, marriage. The chapter on the Christian Church would be interesting—it has been responsible for so much good, it has been guilty of so much evil. The temptation today is indifference. It is so involved in its own affairs that it forgets that it exists to serve others, to wash feet.

We have had a stern warning from our Lord himself. Not orthodoxy, not rubrics, but ministering to the hungry, the thirsty, the naked, the lonely. If it were possible I should like to pass pencil and paper to each of you and ask you to write down what you are doing to bring Christian influence to bear on society. It's easy to be drugged by pious phrases. "Thy Kingdom come, Thy Will be done in *ENGLAND* and in heaven". The truth comes when you have to state in black and white what you are doing to implement these phrases. Let me pinpoint my question: is your church such a hive of industry, so active in the locality that people are aware of its existence? I am not referring to church services, to what happens inside the parish hall, but to secular affairs. Are some of your members on the borough council or local education committee, are you a school manager or governor of a hospital, do you help with the old age pensioners, or the youth clubs, are you a prison visitor or a samaritan, are you active in your employer's federation or your trade union, do you take an interest in housing and if need be lobby your Member of Parliament? God has a purpose for Britain, he wills social justice, and he wants of his Church the co-operation he had from Mary—"behold the hand-maid of the Lord, be it unto me according to thy word". The Kingdom of Heaven in Britain, that is the pattern—we, the

Church, are the handmaids.

Economic change: A churchman in the Southern States of America hit the nail on the head (in the wrong way) when he said "I refuse to share bread with a Negro at the Communion Table because I am not prepared to share bread with him outside". At least he was honest. He knew that the economics of the altar undermine the economics of the acquisitive society. At the altar we have a foretaste of the Kingdom of God— what we have we have in common; there is neither rank nor precedence; nobody receives more than what he needs; there is distinction neither of class nor colour; we are a brotherhood motivated by the spirit of sharing, a holy community.

The conflicts and tensions in the world today, in our own country between the classes, in Africa between white and black, in the world at large between East and West, are basically about *BREAD*, about the resources of the world and how we share them. And we Christians claim to have the answer. We take the bread from the grasping hands of selfish men, and place it in the hands of Christ—that is our offering. And when it is blessed and broken it is given back to us to distribute. Such are the economics of the altar, and we find the Real Presence when bread and wine and all the resources of God's world are used as he means them to be used.

"My soul doth magnify the Lord and my spirit hath rejoiced in God my Sav-

iour." Yes, it is the Magnificat, the song of Mary, that points the way forward. It gives us the programme, moral, social and economic. It provides the criterion by which our activities as Christians shall be judged. And it is my hope that Walsingham will present the message of Mary with such force that it will drive us and thousands more back into the world to crusade for the Kingdom of the Son.

Waste, void, darkness, the Spirit moved, let there be light. God's design for creation persists. Darkness giving place to light, formlessness to form, unconsciousness to consciousness, the first Adam to the second Adam, the Kingdom of this world to the Kingdom of Heaven.

We can help or hinder this design by the quality of our response. What that quality should be is placarded before us during the festival of Pentecost. "Before their eyes appeared tongues like flames which separated off and settled above each of them. They were all filled with the Holy Spirit."

My prayer for you and for me is this, that we should know the Spirit, live in the Spirit, magnify the fruits of the Spirit. *Veni Creator Spiritus*—Come, Holy Ghost, my soul inspire. Please God he will take this prayer at its face value and answer it so that we leave Walsingham with Pentecostal blessings like flames of fire in our hearts. It is only men who live in the Spirit and are consumed with the charity of Christ that can be agents for his Kingdom.

Mary and Pilgrimage

Address by Patrick Rodger, Bishop of Manchester, 31 May 1976, Feast of the Visitation.

'About this time Mary set out and went straight to a town in the uplands of Judah'. It is interesting to notice that among the few references to Our Lady which we have in the Gospels, the great majority show her as being on a journey. The difficult journey during her pregnancy to Bethlehem; the flight into Egypt for survival of her Child; the return to Jerusalem to present the Child in the Temple; the wedding journey to Cana of Galilee; and the tragic journey to Calvary where the promised sword would pierce through her own heart also. You would almost think that Mary was never at home, though no doubt there were happy unrecorded months and years at Nazareth; and we restless modern people, who are 'in journeyings oft' and we pilgrims especially, may here find an affinity with the very one whom we come to honour. It is characteristic of the Christian faith that we do not simply find Our Lord and his Mother at the *end* of our pilgrimage but that, unseen, they accompany us all the way, in the joys and sorrows of travelling, yes in its minor disappointments and ridiculous inconveniences, they are there as well for we may be quite sure that they too had to plan their journeys and that they too knew the trials of heat and cold, hunger and thirst, crowding and noise. The word 'deacon' which has acquired so ecclesiastical a sound over the centuries originally meant 'one who went through the dust' and in that sense both Our Lord and Our Lady were, and are, truly diaconal. They go through the dust of our earthly pilgrimage with us, touched with the feeling of our infirmities, as the Letter to the Hebrews so beautifully says.

Some of you may perhaps have read Zoe Oldenburg's story of the First Crusade which is called *The Heirs of the Kingdom*. In purely historical terms, it is a tragedy of the highest order. It tells how some simple people from the north of France gave up their homes and their livelihood to 'take the cross'; how they journeyed amid labours and sufferings that we can hardly imagine nowadays; and how they became caught up in a terrible war which damaged Christendom, let alone the infidels, for centuries. They had been given a vision of Jerusalem which was, as we should say 'out of this world' and so when they reached the end of their pilgrimage and saw the object of their hopes and dreams, the shock of disappointment was almost unbearable, and the reader can hardly keep himself from weeping on their behalf. Yet of course this is only one part—not even the main part—of the meaning of that story. For Jesus Christ was not confined to the city of Jerusalem as an object to be visited at the end of the journey. 'Believe me' he said 'the time is coming when you will worship the Father neither on this mountain, nor in Jerusalem. . .but the time is already here when the real worshippers will worship the Father in spirit and in truth'. The pilgrims of the First Crusade, whether they knew it or not, had had the presence of their Lord with them 'in spirit and in truth'—had had the company of the Blessed Virgin Mary and all the saints—from the very moment they set out on their journey and at every stage of joy or suffering on the road. The thousands who died before they ever set eyes on the earthly Jerusalem were upheld and befriended by those invisible Presences, and what they longed for and greeted from afar was in truth no fortress occupied by the Saracens but 'the city which has foundations, whose builder and maker is God'. Was this not the *true* meaning of their pilgrimage long ago and does it not speak to our condition too, in the vastly different outward circumstances of England in 1976?

Not long ago, the Doctrine Commission of the Church of England published a report, which began by describing the Christian life as a journey, a voyage of exploration, into the heart of Love itself. Those who think that the prime job of Doctrine Commissions is to restate dogmatic certainties have had few good words to say for that report—and of course one *can* represent the kind of Christianity which it advocates as a mere 'making it all up as you go along'. Nevertheless, the image of the Christian life as a journey has the oldest and most respectable antecedents. If one may dare to mention John Bunyan at Walsingham, there was *Pilgrim's Progress*—but long, long before that the Church itself was described as 'the Way' (do we think of it now as 'the Way' or simply as 'the Halt'?). Most important of all, the Lord of the Church declares 'I *am* the Way. . .' Men had often pictured God as the Alpha and Omega, the beginning and end of their mortal journey, the One in whom at last they would find their rest. What was different about the Word made flesh was that he accompanied the travellers on their journey, 'through the dust' but the Emmaus story tells us that 'their eyes were holden and they did not know him' or in the limpid prose of the N.E.B. 'something kept them from seeing who it was'. It was only after he had broken bread for them that their eyes were opened. So many, many miles do we go on our earthly pilgrimage before we open our eyes and exclaim: 'But the Son of God Himself was with us all the time!'

Today we are commemorating one of the most joyful—perhaps *the* most joyful of the journeys of Our Lady. On the face of it, it was quite an ordinary one. You can imagine what they said casually in Nazareth: 'Where's Mary gone?' 'Oh, to visit those old cousins of hers—you know the parson and his wife who live in the hill country'. But Mary, as we know, carried with her a secret so great, news so stupendous, that she herself must have felt ready to explode with mingled astonishment and terror, but above all joy and excitement. She needed to seek out an older woman, but not just any old person. Perhaps Elisabeth was the kind of person you sought out in a crisis anyway, but it seemed from God's message to her that Elisabeth too was involved in these strange and marvellous happenings. So it was Elisabeth that she must see without delay—and maybe, only maybe, she could explain to her the great unbelievable news; news at which other people would only be likely to stare and laugh as if she were mad, or else sternly tell her not to be guilty of blasphemous presumption. And who could blame them?

But when she reached the end of her journey, Elisabeth came out to meet her and there was nothing to explain after all. Her great news was already known and believed and celebrated with a burst of joy! 'God's blessing is on you above all women, and his blessing is on the fruit of your womb!' Mary and Elisabeth recognised one another immediately as within the purpose of God who had chosen them. For all the sorrows that would later afflict them, they recognised in one another a joy that could never be forgotten. And this, St. Luke tells us, was the moment of the Magnificat, that triumphant song which the Church sings to this day.

So the journey of those who love Jesus Christ and who follow Him in the way is not an aimless affair, even if there are times when we seem to get lost and to have to retrace a great many steps. I spoke about our modern journeying, and in this age, it often seems to be fairly purposeless—keeping in rapid motion just for the sake of it. (Perhaps that is why we continue to invent ever quicker ways of travel at vast public expense while a bus ride begins to be too costly for the ordinary family)

In Christian language, however, our human journey is known as a pilgrimage; and a pilgrimage by definition, is never aimless and never solitary either. We undertake it with serious intent, after thought and prayer. We have companions who don't merely travel beside us but often enrich our whole understanding of the way we are treading and of the object of our journey. And there also goes with us, before us the object of our journey. And there goes with us, or before us, that unseen Companion who leads and preserves our steps, often when we think of him least, Jesus Christ, the way, the truth and the life. But surely the greatest joy of all is that the news we carry, however improbable it may seem to our neighbours at home is recognised and shared in this company so that what we thought was something secret and private (and perhaps absurd) is multiplied a thousand fold, so that it becomes our door into the unending joy of God Himself. Blessed are those who travel with news and with unfailing hope! Blessed are those who are called to the marriage-feast of the Lamb!

Mary prays

Address at the National Pilgrimage 1978, by Bishop Michael Ramsey

II Corinthians 13, 12. The grace of our Lord Jesus Christ and the love of God and the fellowship of the Holy Spirit be with you.

We have all come here' to Walsingham longing for the renewal of the Christian Church, of all Christians, of ourselves. We ask Mary and the Saints to pray for this renewal. When we do so we are not asking that their prayers will be instead of our prayers. No, we join our own prayers with the prayers of Mary within the one praying family in heaven, in paradise, and on earth. Thus our asking for the prayers of Mary is inseparable from our own calling to be saints, and it is in the realisation that Christians everywhere are called to be saints that the Church can be renewed.

What words, in our small understanding, describe better the prayer of Mary, the prayer of the saints and the prayer of us all than the words of the apostle Paul "The grace of our Lord Jesus Christ and the love of God and the fellowship of the Holy Spirit be with you."? Words so simple, so familiar, let today renew us in their simplicity and their mighty power.

"The grace of our Lord Jesus Christ." His grace means his personal impact upon human lives which does not leave them the same. See our Lord in Galilee. To some who are stricken with sin and guilt he brings divine forgiveness. To some, too proud and complacent to know their sins, he brings disturbance of their conscience. To those who are filled with bewilderment and fear in face of the world's distress he brings trust and serenity. To the lonely he brings the knowledge that they are loved and cared for. Such is the grace of our Lord Jesus Christ. It made, and makes, people different. The ministry of Jesus leads on to Calvary, and Calvary is the mightiest of all manifestations of the grace of our Lord, bringing for all time the confrontation between God's judgement and compassion and the sinfulness of the human race. Then comes Easter, and the Risen Jesus still continues the impact of his grace through word and sacrament. We want to help people to realise that the sacramental life of the Holy Catholic Church is not a cumbrous addition to a simple gospel, for it simply means Jesus himself continuing his mighty work of grace amongst human lives. But we help others to realise this if we know ourselves that every Mass we attend and every Communion we receive should make us different for the grace of our Lord Jesus Christ is there. To be different, to begin to learn holiness, that is what the grace of Jesus is about.

"The love of God." All this concerning Jesus, his life and death and resurrection, happens because it is God's own gift to the world. God so loved that he gave the gift of Jesus. The love of God is the source of it all. And in giving Jesus, God was giving his own very self, Immanuel, God with us. The debate about the Incarnation is partly about what sort of Christ we believe in, and through the centuries the heart of the Christian faith is that without idolatry we worship Jesus as divine. The debate is also about what kind of God we believe in: is he just a God who sends servants, messengers, prophets, Jesus being one of this long series, or is he a God who gives his own very self to mankind? Our Christian God is a God who gives nothing less than himself. He gives himself to his own created world to restore it, he gives himself to humanity to complete the union with himself of humanity made in his own image, he gives himself to share in the world's darkness and agony and to take the burden upon himself. Immanuel, God with us. May today bring home to us the depth of our faith in the Incarnation and its moral and spiritual significance.

"The Fellowship of the Holy Spirit". The first believers were overwhelmed by the revelation of God in Christ and were moved to make their response. But how could they respond to so stupendous a thing? Their response, and our response too, is by the divine power and person given to be within them, the Holy Spirit. They prayed to God as Father with new conviction because the Holy Spirit in them was crying Abba, Father. They called Jesus Lord and deepened their allegiance to him, because the Holy Spirit in them enabled them to say "Jesus is Lord". This did not, and does not, happen in any individual isolation, for the Spirit who unites us to Christ does so by uniting us also to one another in sharing of heart and mind and life. Such is the Fellowship of the Holy Spirit.

How wonderfully simple is the faith of the Holy Catholic Church, the faith of Father, Son and Spirit; until we complicate it by our muddles, our heresies and our sins. But its simplicity is a very costly simplicity, so we say "Mary pray for us, and let us pray with you".

What may we learn and what may we draw from Mary's own example?

Obedience. "Behold the handmaid of the Lord, be it unto me according to thy word." Obedience has become a kind of missing element in our modern religion. There can be no holiness without the recovery of obedience. Mary pray for us.

Adoration. "My soul doth magnify the Lord". Adoration is the magnifying of God in the forgetfulness of self. Alas we tend to magnify things that are worthless or second-rate, and worst of all we try to magnify our own little selves, selves which are infinitesimal little creatures beside the majesty of God. Mary pray for us.

Intercession. We pass on to Cana of Galilee. "The Mother of Jesus said to him, they have no wine." She notices a need and speaks to Jesus about it. Perhaps intercession is too formal and too pious a word for the quiet observing and caring about the needs of people, great or small, and sharing our noticing and our caring with our Lord. The answer to our caring is the work of Christ's new creation: water into wine, the new creation is at work, water into wine. Christ will recreate the world for he is himself the One born by the Holy Spirit's overshadowing Mary to be the Mother. Mary pray for us.

All this however, the obedience, the adoration, the prayer, leads on to the Hill of Calvary. On that Hill there stand near the Cross, Mary the Mother and John the Apostle. From Calvary there comes the mighty power of the grace of our Lord, of the love of God, of the fellowship of the Spirit. So Mary pray for us, John pray for us, and may we know more deeply the grace of our Lord Jesus Christ, the love of God and the Fellowship of the Holy Spirit. Alleluia. Amen.

Mary and Renewal

Address given by Dr Robert Runcie the Archbishop of Canterbury at Walsingham 26 May 1980.

St. Luke, chapter 1, verse 38.
"And Mary said, I am the Lord's. As you have said, so be it."

I have come here today because you are a lively lot—of all ages—and you share with me enthusiasm for the Spirit of Jesus Christ.

You've come from all over England on May 26th when in our Calendar we commemorate St. Augustine of Canterbury, to pray that we in our day may follow him in spreading that Spirit through our Nation.

We come as individual pilgrims to this remote village, known for centuries as England's Nazareth, home of Mary—to discover in our hearts that Jesus lives.

Two weeks ago I stood in the open air at a football stadium in Africa. The occasion—the birthday of an Anglican Province—at my side, the Archbishop of Uganda supported by the Bishops of that brave Church. Before us was the new Archbishop about to be enthroned on a simple wooden chair to the accompaniment of song and dance.

It was in this part of Africa that an Evangelical-revival has taken place. The spiritual fruits of that experience are evident today, not least throughout troubled Uganda.

Today at Walsingham I am celebrating in the open air—different circumstances, different customs—and I remember the advice given by Gregory to St. Augustine: "Teach the Church of the English what you have been able to gather from other Churches. For things are not to be loved for the sake of a place; but places are to be loved for their good things".

Augustine was told by Gregory to be gentle about strange but cherished customs. "As long as there is unity in the Faith, differences in custom do not damage the Holy Church".

At this Eucharist in this holy place we first give witness to that Unity in the Faith which we enjoy.

So often in the past, and even today, we misunderstand each other, deny each other, and even curse each other because we have lost sight of the one thing necessary.

Our Unity lies in our common Faith, and our Faith lies in the Risen Lord Jesus Christ.

Pope John Paul II and this Archbishop of Canterbury were able recently to say with one voice that they were glad "their meeting took place in Africa where the rapid expansion and the self-sacrificing zeal of the Church and the visible enthusiasm and love for Our Lord Jesus Christ has many lessons for Christians in Europe."

The experience of Christianity in Africa and the Walsingham Pilgrimage will be lost to those who deal only in words and debate.

We live in a society which trusts overmuch in words, organisation, activism. Mary reminds us that quietness, longing, receptivity to the Word of God are the beginnings of growth in the Gospel.

In the TV film *Jesus of Nazareth,* I found that amidst much show-biz glamour there was a very moving moment—the agelong attempt to portray the Annunciation—no angels with gauzy wings but a rainbow and Mary's puzzled but resolute "I will be the Lord's". In that moment, beauty, simplicity, mystery, tragedy and triumph mingled to capture the most intimate encounter of the soul with

God. Here in this moment is a message of hope for the hopeless, a message of hope for a world torn by selfishness and greed. Despite our sins, mankind is worthwhile in God's eyes. God gives himself to us so that, like Mary, we can be Christ-bearers.

What Mary receives she shares. That is why in scripture and tradition Mary is a welcoming figure. In the churches of Eastern Europe which I know so well you have the figure of Mary in the apse, above, Christ reigns in glory. Mary welcomes you to the realm where Christ reigns whatever the conditions outside.

Our anxious activism springs from fear; but when you come to Faith in Christ there is ultimate security. That's why Mary stands for the family virtues of acceptance, forgiveness, companionship which give a person anchorage in life and without which they cannot grow.

But that security does not promise safety. The secure person is the one who can be free to take risks for the Faith. From Faith springs obedience. "As you have said, so be it."

On the eve of the martyrdom of Archbishop Luwum in Uganda 3 years ago, a missionary had a dream. He dreamt he was looking across a vast plain. In the distance he saw a fire. As he approached the fire he saw in the midst of the flames an African. To his surprise the body was not being consumed. Then he heard a voice which invited him to put his own hands in the flames.

We are not all called to dramatic martyrdom, but you who enjoy the security offered by Our Lord are to be touched by the flame of the Spirit and you will be changed and not destroyed.

But you will look at life in a fresh way—the dream of fire portrays a mixture of hope and sorrow, just as in Mary we see suffering and the joy of one who sings "Tell out my soul the gladness of the Lord".

The theme of joy through sorrow is a fundamental experience of Christian faith. It reflects death and resurrection. Christianity is now about simple happiness—the good fortune that comes from good health, a good income, a good marriage—of course we are meant to enjoy such gifts, but alas they don't come to us all and they are often short lived. The deepest and richest experiences of life come when something which is askew is faced and overcome, and there emerges something stronger and more deeply joyful.

You must have known that yourselves coming through, or seeing it, in a bereavement, a broken marriage, a mistaken decision—so that out of it comes a triumph which proclaims that life, whatever comes, can never defeat you.

Mary speaks to us of all these things because she speaks to us through devotion, through song, through relationships and through trials, of Christ and His Church:

Welcoming and forgiving.
Praying and receiving.
Obedient and compassionate.
Confident and joyful.

These are the qualities needed for the renewal of the Church and the spread of the Gospel.

And to those of you who love Walsingham and honour the home of Mary, and find a place here where Jesus lives, take away these gifts and share them. Don't allow your love of this place to build a Church which is:

Exclusive and judging.
Unready to listen and change.
Trivial and insensitive.
Fearful and defensive.

That doesn't sound like a church on the move.

141

Across the world, the Lord is renewing His Church in China, in Africa, in places like Taize or Iona, as well as in Pastoral Congresses in Liverpool. Walsingham can be part of that renewal if every pilgrim can truly say with Mary:

"I am the Lord's. As you have said, so be it."

"Behold, Your Mother" John 19,27

Sermon by Timothy Bavin, Bishop of Portsmouth, at the National Pilgrimage on Monday 25 May 1987.

No matter what word is used—mother or mater, mummy or mum, mammy, mam, mommy or mom, or just plain ma—there is no denying that it has for most of us a rich emotional content. For a mother's bond with her child is a unique and lasting one which cannot be supplied by the father or other relation, however close. A step-mother does her best, in spite of the pantomime's cruelty to her reputation, and mothers-in-law have had their role undermined by music hall. Aunts are useful and amusing, but they have nearly always to be treated with great respect; whilst sisters, cousins and sweethearts lack the *gravitas* which we expect in a mother.

So there is nothing quite like a mother, whether she be plain, grand- or great-grand-, and there are few who do not experience an indefinable warmth at the very mention of motherhood.

The direst burglar Bill had "Mother" in a blue and red heart tattooed on his bulging biceps; the little old lady treasures her seaside brooch with "Mother" proclaimed on its tawdry face, given by a child long since dead; birthday greetings are all sugar and satin in the "Mother" section of the card shop; Mothering Sunday will always attract widespread and spontaneous support, no matter what is written in the *Church Times;* and our nation experiences a rare unanimity in its common love for the Mother of our Queen.

It might be said, then, that all the world loves a mother.

That being so, it is surprising that the Church in this land has generally underrated the significance and value of the Mother of our Lord. True, she has more than one feast or commemoration in our calendar, but, as members of the Church of England, we are not expected or encouraged to give her too prominent a place in either our spirituality or our proclamation. In part, this is a legacy from the Reformation's reaction to perhaps an excess of Marian devotion; and maybe part is to be attributed to the Anglo-Saxon dislike of being too emotional or demonstrative, particularly in the practice of religion.

As a result, our theology, our preaching and our worship are on the whole rather coldly respectable, decent, moderate—and, as often as not, lacking the conviction and infectiousness which a more emotional involvement would arouse. There's not much passion about most of it, and whilst we rightly feel deeply about issues of human justice, it seems that it's not quite nice to be emotional, extravagant, or even vulgar, in our experience and expression of the Faith.

Thus, doctrinal debates are conducted largely at a cerebral level; only that which is consistent with Scripture is to be taught for salvation; and the ASB or other forms of worship are approved only if they can be shown to be strictly orthodox. Add to that the thoroughly good taste of our Church interiors and most of our music, and it is small wonder that we are generally considered to be comfortably "middle-class".

Even Catholic liturgy and devotion have been tailored to accord with 20th century rationalism, and for some it's a rare thrill to come across a pre-Vatican II image or Tridentine High Mass—not just for old times' sake, but because they appeal to the emotions and recognise that there's more to the Gospel than an exercise of the intellect. For Faith surely involves at least as much emotion as reason, and the truth of our religion is to be apprehended with the heart as well as with the head.

Jesus knew that, and most of His teaching was directed at people who had little or no learning but who responded to the ordinary appeal of the sower or shepherd, the widow or wastrel, the master or merchant; there were birds, flowers, weeds, bread, salt and lanterns, everyday things and everyday people. No great education or analysis were needed for the message to get across.

Many centuries later those heroic priests of the industrial revolution's slums knew that more was required than preaching—no matter how eloquent—for their people to respond to the call of Christ. So they filled their churches with movement, decoration and colour: "extraordinary" devotions, "nasty" pictures, "ghastly" stained glass and "awful" statues. Worship was designed to appeal to the eye, the ear and the nose, as well as to the brain. No matter that it was vulgar and often over the top; no matter that it went contrary to Reformation formularies: it brought people to a love of Our Lord and into His Kingdom—and that, after all, is why the Church exists.

The beauty of holiness in worship remains one of the requirements for effective evangelism in our own day. But if we are to reach the majority of this country's people who are untouched by the Gospel, that beauty is going to have to be much more "popular" and far less antiseptic than most of us here would

prefer. It will need to be as unashamed as the tabloids in appealing to the *feelings* of people who have put "Dallas", "Dynasty" and "Eastenders" at the top of the ratings.

So the correct, but rather flat, English of the NEB won't do; nor will much of our tidy but somewhat clinical ordering of worship and the safe musical and literary standards of the New English Hymnal (admirable as is that book). Hymns in particular are important as expressing and teaching popular devotion and there's many a one which has come into expert disfavour because of "bad" poetry or a mawkish tune, which nevertheless goes on being sung because—in spite of words or music—it still reaches parts of you which other hymns don't reach. Nor should we overlook that where people do respond in good numbers to evangelism, that is nearly always in a congregation or assembly where the language is frankly sentimental ("Sweet Jesus", "Precious Saviour") and where the music falls far short of the standards of the Royal School of Church Music. As one who regards himself as having impeccable Anglican aesthetic appreciation, and who would find it difficult to cope with what he is saying, I do not suggest the abandonment of what is decent, distinctive and excellent in our tradition. But I do plead that the Church of England should rediscover her heart and make greater appeal to the emotions of the nation, for the sake of the Gospel. If St. Paul could become all things to all people in order, by all means, to save some (I Cor. 9,22), it is surely possible for our Church, by the grace of God, to overcome the cultural and intellectual inhibitions to evangelism, to bring people to Christ which is what its mission is all about.

So let's be a bit batty and extravagant in our devotion, as a complement and counterbalance to the dullness of moderation. Let grown men weep, as Jesus wept; let The Peace erupt into an orgy of physical contact by Christians—

143

after all, for some of us it will be the only time in the week when we are touched by another human being; let some of those dreadful soupy hymns and choruses be exhumed from the dust of vestry cupboards for a joyful and heartfelt noise to the Lord.

But above all, let the Blessed Virgin Mary find a place once more in our popular devotion, even if statues, oleographs, candles and rosaries are out of fashion. For, as Mother of the Lord, she is Mother also of the Church; she is your Mother and my Mother and, as Mother of this nation, she surely iongs to draw its men, women and children to the obedience of her Son. Moreover, she gave birth to One who was fully human, with all our emotions and whose emotional response to His Mother is recorded in the Gospel we heard just now. There is no doubt of His feelings at that moment and if we do not identify ourselves with those feelings we are, I suggest, guilty of an act of impiety which in fact detracts from our devotion to the Lord.

"Shall we not love thee, Mother dear,
Whom Jesus loves so well?"

Yes indeed,

"And as He loves thee, Mother dear,
We too will love thee well;
And, to His glory, year by year,
Thy joy and honour tell."

AMÉN

Mary—the Woman

Sara Maitland

In sincere and proper devotion to Our Lady Queen of Heaven, the Mystic Rose, the Star of the Sea (and sometimes of course in sentimental escapism from the realities of sexuality and the demands of justice) we can too easily lose sight of the humanity of Mary, Mother of Jesus. And this is wrong because as Incarnationalists (read Christians) we know that it is only the sinless life that we have seen that can make real for us the glorified life that we have not yet seen.

Mary does not get massive coverage in the Bible, but whenever she does appear it is for two purposes—to reveal more about the glory of God or to show us the fully lived, perfect human life, the most complete response to God possible. To see what this can mean for us now, we must try sometimes to look not at the Assumed, Crowned, Glorified Queen but at who she was before. This is not easy for two reasons: firstly she was a member of precisely that group (women of the peasant or working classes) which history has most consistently ignored; and secondly because our mental image of her has been influenced by some of the most beautiful art of the Western world. But some facts are possible: she was a semitic Arab girl from the impoverished North of the insignificant Roman province of Palestine and therefore probably mal-nourished, almost certainly illiterate, destined by law and social custom to be given in marriage while still an adolescent to a man somewhat older than herself, to become his legal property and bear his children in quiet anonymity until her death at about the age of 35. The gospel account bears out some of this; she was already engaged to a skilled manual labourer or minor artisan. Then, suddenly, God asked her to participate in a preposterous plan: despite being a virgin she was going to get pregnant by the direct action of the Holy Spirit. Her response to this proposal was brief (one verse: Luke 1:38) and absolute: with her whole person she agreed completely, and opened herself entirely to God's will.

But this is not all. Without a break Luke reports that she went "with haste" to visit her cousin Elizabeth. Luke offers no explanation for this rather curious trip, though on the face of it to go rushing off to visit distant and elderly relatives in the early weeks of unexpected pregnancies is at least unusual. Is it wrong to speculate that she needed to talk things over with this other woman who was having not dissimilar experiences? (The Women's Liberation Consciousness-raising groups have confirmed among women how valuable this can be.) We do know that Jesus, after his baptism when the holy Spirit was poured over him, was immediately seized by temptations about his vocation. Perhaps the same is true for Mary. There was Joseph's peculiar behaviour to think about; at first he had acted, alas, normally enough—he certainly didn't want to marry someone else's "used goods". But then he changed his mind and now wants to marry her. Why? Can she rightly get married? To him? Does he fully realise what sort of marriage she feels it will have to be? And what are the neighbours saying? And her own parents, who have always had such high hopes for their only daughter, what are they thinking, feeling, suffering? It was not an easy problem for a teenager to take to the local priests: Judaism was not noted for either its sexual liberalism or for its tolerance towards female presumption. Perhaps she went to Elizabeth just to get away from home, or as a last resort. But the consequences of her going were something very wonderful. Just as Mary had demonstrated the perfect response to God's direct call, now she and Elizabeth demonstrate for us the perfect working of Christian fellowship. For Elizabeth's immediate, inspired, unsought greeting confirms and affirms Mary, liberates her from any doubts, frees her for the first time into joy, and she pours out the glorious poem we now know as the Magnificat. She praises God from her heart; through praise she recognises her own self, beloved of God, and the true glory of her vocation (neither pride nor false modesty can mar this moment of self-knowledge); and from this recognition and the realisation of what it says about God's very nature she can prophesy about how that God will deal with all the rest of oppressed humanity in love and faithfulness and justice. This little vignette from Luke is one of the purest examples of what the Church should be: a community of love where everyone encourages each other in their own gifts and vocations in order to build up each other and the whole Church.

This passage from Luke is the only sustained Marian narrative in the New Testament, and it is only 30 verses long. It is, in a complete sense, enough. For the rest of the Gospel story she makes only fleeting or group appearances: this in itself says something about the nature of vocation, but it is possible to say more, not just about Christian response but also specifically about a Christian woman's response. Mary's gender, and sex, is emphasised not denied by her particular vocation and women have both a privilege and a duty to look at her and see what it means to be a woman filled with God. Lots has been written about this, much of which I would not want to question, but if the Spirit is going to have a chance to lead us into all truth we must keep on and on looking for more. Here are a few glimpses of Mary, which I, a Christian woman in the 1980s, have found helpful in seeking my own Christian lifestyle:

Mary was an uneducated girl whose desire to understand God, not just with her heart but with her intelligence as well, freed her to cross-question the Archangel Gabriel in person.

Mary was a woman who, because of her understanding of her own vocation, contracted a marriage radically different from the social *and religious* norms of her time (ever-virginity, no more children.)

Mary was a woman with so little sense of personal pride that she, lovingly, put up with continual public humiliation and even impertinence from the younger person she recognised as her Teacher, even though he was her own son and 'owed' her respect.

Mary was a woman so little bound by conventional morality that far from objecting to her son consorting with a known prostitute, actually made a friend of the woman and shared with her the most intimate tasks connected with her own child's dead body.

Mary was a woman with so little sense of public shame or fear that she stood openly under the gallows on which her criminal son was being hung.

Mary was a mother so unexclusively 'family minded' that, while her only son was dying by inches before her eyes, she was able to redirect herself and enter into a new motherly relationship with John.

Mary was a widow with so little dignity that after the death of her son, instead of returning home to the protection of her family, she hung about in Jerusalem with a bunch of layabouts.

Mary was a woman of such faith that she did not need to see the resurrected Christ in order to believe.

Mary was a woman who, from the very start of her vocation, identified herself with the poor, the hungry and the oppressed, and extended her loving mothering to the bereft, the persecuted—and thence to the infant church itself.

Mary is the full free human who proclaims in her every known action that the life of God-created women is not to be dictated by the laws or social customs of the times, but by the knowledge of God and the knowledge of self-in-God alone. Mary, Theotokos—"the God bearer", proclaims that this is done by letting God grow in our female flesh and giving that God again openly to the world.

Our Lady of Walsingham and Christian Unity

At the heart of the Catholic Revival in the Church of England there has always been a longing for the reunion of the Churches. Prayer for reunion has been part of pilgrims' devotions from the start. Father Hope Patten shared the vision of Father Fynes-Clinton who founded what became the Anglican and Eastern Churches Association in 1906, and the Church Unity Octave Council in 1921 and was also a leading member of the Catholic League. The League, established in July 1913 to promote unity with the See of S. Peter came on pilgrimage to Walsingham annually from 1927. An Orthodox chapel was part of the original plan for the extensions to the Shrine in 1938. The Roman Catholics established their own Shrine at the Slipper Chapel in 1934 and relations were not easy in the early years but common devotion to our Lady, and the prayers of our Lady herself, have drawn the two shrines together, especially since the Second Vatican Council.

If England is ever to be reconverted: if these Provinces are ever to be reunited to their parent stock, devotion to Mary must become widely accepted among us, for it is impossible to hold the true Faith apart from Our Lady. She is the instrument all through the divine plan of redemption; leaving out the Mother of God it is impossible to begin to get a right understanding of God Himself or the meaning of salvation. It is because Mary is so patently left out in the scheme of English religious teaching that thousands, nay millions, of our countrymen have no grasp of the first principles of Christianity. Walsingham, therefore, has a real place in the scheme not only of restoring the fundamental principles of the Faith, but in preparing for the outward reunion of Christendom.

A. Hope Patten

Mary and Prayer for Unity

THERE is a close connection between Walsingham and prayer for Christian unity. Since this is the duty of all christians, why should it be especially so for the sodales of the Holy House? For several reasons.

Every Anglican pilgrim to Walsingham prays for unity among Christians, either in the Pilgrimage Church or when Pope Benedict XV's prayers are said in the roadway outside the Slipper Chapel. For our Lady originally had, and still wills to have, but one shrine at Walsingham. Yet she has two; and the two do not do her a double honour, but rather diminish her glory, because they are really the one shrine of other ages now split in two by the Christians who ought to be joining together in propagating its honour. The joy of every pilgrimage (for joy is the natural atmosphere of Mary's house) is shot through with the pain of the difference between Anglican and Roman, so that here, as perhaps nowhere else in England, the sense of division is poignant and over-whelming. Mary's children are divided in her own house, and cannot join together in loving homage there. How much more painful is the thought of those many English Christians who are so far cut off from their brethren as never even to wish to come and honour their heavenly Mother in

147

either shrine at Englands's Nazareth! We can feel the sword that pierced her heart: for the sins of schism are among those sins of ours which crucified Jesus and pierced the immaculate heart of Mary.

But if we feel the acute sorrow of the division of Christendom at Walsingham, in our own shrine, at least, we can find some cause for thanksgiving as well, in the constant prayer that is offered there for the repairing of the breaches. The Guardians of the shrine have always recognized that one of its chief works is prayer for unity: so we have the Orthodox Chapel in the Pilgrimage Church, with its groups of Orthodox pilgrims, and the insistence on prayer for unity, at every pilgrimage. We have the Council of the Church Unity Octave placing its work under the patronage of Our Lady of Walsingham. An important part in the increase of widespread prayer for unity has been development in the cultus of our Lady at the shrine. We owe God thanks for all this. And we have seen the shrine authorities arrange a pilgrimage of reparation for new schisms, made in the name of "Re-union" in South India, showing a concern for the true unity of the Church and not merely for a convenient merging of denominations. For that, too, we must thank God.

For the unity among Christians is the burning desire of the heart of our Lord. On the eve of His death, His prayer to His Father was for the unity of His disciples: "Father, that they may all be one, as thou art in me and I in thee." The heart of Mary, perfectly one with the heart of Jesus, burns with the same fervour for this union. Those who love her and would unite their wills with hers must learn the same longing and devotion for unity among Christians.

Mary certainly wills that Christians should be re-united with all the power of her heart. The love of Mary for individual souls, and her love for Christ, move her intercession on behalf of the Church; and her intercession is part of the life of the Church, as we sing in the Salve Re-gina. It is our duty to join in that intercession, to fulfil the life of the Church, to pray with her. But prayer with Mary must also be prayer through Mary. So our prayer for reunion must be prayer through Mary. It is a little surprising that the fine Walsingham prayer (Mary, recall the solemn moment) does not contain among the petitions at the end any prayer for unity. Perhaps we may be permitted to hope that it may one day be inserted there.

But in all our prayer for unity we must be careful to pray in the most perfect possible conformity to the wishes of Jesus and Mary. That means we must remember that prayer for unity is a missionary prayer and a great prayer of charity. It must not be a prayer that God will work unity as we want it done, working our will; but that God's will may be gloriously and perfectly fulfilled. In his mercy and love he reveals that will to us; and we know that we can safely fulfil it by imitating Mary. Her only concern is God's will.

Mary was made Mother of all when from the Cross Jesus gave her himself in his mystical body, which is to include all Christians, in the person of John. Her concern is thus a motherly concern not only for the unity of Anglicans with the Holy See, but of all Christians, including every variety of Protestant and every heretic, in the one body of her Son, according to his will. It means, also, the incorporation of all those who do not know the salvation of Jesus into this same one body of his. Mary loves all because she is Mother of the whole Christ, and we are all in Christ, and the whole Christ includes all the elect. Mary's prayer embraces all: our prayer with her and through her must also embrace all. Our charity must emulate the width and depth of her charity, in prayer for all Christians and in prayer for more Christians—prayer for more Christians because the first fruit of unity must be increased fertility of the Church in bringing new souls to rebirth in baptism for the missionary conquest of the world by Christ the King.

Mary is the perfect prayer in her charity toward man and God, and as she is the supreme model for all our prayer and spiritual life, so she is the model of our prayer for unity. It is easy for us to pray a little during the week of prayer for Christian unity every January, and join in the occasional devotions for this intention which are given us when on pilgrimage and at various other times. These petitions are valuable in the sight of God, but they are not completely conformed to Mary's prayer. The example of Mary in the life of Nazareth and Jerusalem shows a different attitude. Father Boylan has called that life "ordinary, obscure and laborious." That is an adequate description also of the lives of most Christians: but Mary's is the ordinary life sanctified by perfect prayer. As she is our model, we shall be able to look to her ordinary life as a pattern by which to fashion our own. A whole life turned into prayer: that is the standard which Mary gives us to live up to—a careful consecration of every moment of our lives to fulfilling the will of God for us, the perfect union of Jesus and Mary. In our own days this doctrine has been most magnificently taught by the life and example of S. Theresa of Lisieux. We have seen her turning every little action, every small annoyance and inconvenience into a way of glorifying God, making a confident offering to merciful Love. Pope Benedict XV declared that this was not a doctrine for nuns only, but for every Christian soul. It is, indeed, the aim of every Christian soul to convert its whole existence into the glory of God. And less than ten years ago, an Italian Trappist nun, named after our Lady, in a monastery dedicated to her, embraced that life to the full, offering her whole being in hidden and silent prayer for the return of all the separated brethren to the unity of Christ's church. She died a holy death, entirely dedicated to God's glory with this especial intention.

Many souls have been influenced by S. Theresa of Lisieux, and seen their daily lives transformed by following in her "little way". In the Church of England she is not popular, except among "the most extreme." Yet her kind of prayer, like that of the Trappist nun, is the kind of prayer which is most in union with Mary's prayer. Maybe all Christians are not called, as these holy nuns were, to share Mary's martyrdom at the Cross of Christ in a life and death of intense agony; but all are called to share in this selfless consecration of their daily life of tedious routine, which was Mary's life in Nazareth. It is the fitting way for those who are devoted to England's Nazareth; and there is no better way of joining in Mary's work for unity.

Do not pray for reunion just when public prayers are offered. Every time we say in the Hail Mary, "Pray for us sinners", we implicitly mention the sin of schism.

Remember it often; implore Mary for reunion: use the unity prayer to our Lady of Perpetual Succour for the Orthodox; use the Memorare of S. Bernard: pray to Mary for Protestants; and for a sanctification of Catholics; pray for the fulfilment of the glorious will of God. Consecrated to Mary, as every member of S.O.L.W. is, the soul is consecrated to prayer for unity.

Blessed Mary, Lady of Walsingham, pray for the peace of the household of God.

In 1961 the Master, Father Colin Stephenson visited Rome and had a private audience with Pope John XXIII

The year has started for me in a very exciting way, as on January 23rd I was granted a long private audience with the Pope, and was able to tell him a lot about Walsingham and show him photographs of the Shrine and gain his interest and prayers.

It is a wonderful thing that the Holy Father made the Shrine his intention for his Mass and offices for a whole day.

I went to the Vatican wearing my Guardian's Star which caused great interest, and not long after mid-day I was taken through the various rooms where the guards, chamberlains and gentlemen-in-waiting are in attendance, and reached the Pope's private library. It is customary to genuflect three times on approaching and leaving the Holy Father, but I had no sooner entered the room than he came towards me and led me by the hand to a chair beside his desk.

He began by asking me if my name had anything to do with St. Stephen, and said that as St. Stephen must have known Our Lady, it was very appropriate that a son of St. Stephen should be in charge of one of her shrines. We talked for some time about the need for unity amongst Christians, and the Holy Father emphasised that the things which already unite us are far more important than the things which divide us, and he was most emphatic in his opinion that a common devotion to Our Lady would be one of the most potent forces in bringing us together, and as he spoke he several times made a gesture towards an exquisite picture of Our Lady which was upon his desk, and which was obviously an object of great devotion to him.

He expressed great admiration for the photographs of the Shrine, and asked many searching questions about its organization and the devotions of pilgrimage, particularly as to whether pilgrims made their confessions. Finally he said, "Now we must both of us work and pray that one day it may be possible for me to come and visit this Shrine in person."

He sent his blessing to all who work for the Shrine, and then he said "I would wish my blessing to rest upon all who visit this Shrine, not as exerting authority, but in all simplicity", and he said this with great earnestness.

When I had knelt for his blessing he said "My word, you are a very big **man**. It will take me all my time to fill you **with** blessings." He gave me a medal in a leather case and rosaries and medals for those at the Shrine, particularly choosing white ones for the Sisters and asking their names.

I left feeling very happy, and thinking how proud Fr. Hope Patten would have been to have seen his work make such a marked impression upon the Sovereign Pontiff.

To meet Pope John is an invigorating experience as he radiates kindness and charity, and obviously longs to be at peace and in unity with all Christians, and would far rather minimize differences than force the gap between himself and those out of communion with the Holy See.

The role of our Lady in the restoration of unity in the Church has often been alluded to in sermons in Walsingham.*

Sermon by Fr. Francis Dalby, Superior General, S.S.J.E.
in the Abbey Grounds at Walsingham—Whit-Monday, 1961

Text: S. Luke I:38. "And Mary said, Behold the handmaid of the Lord; be it unto me according to thy word."

As is a speck of dust in a sunbeam in comparison to the sun in whose radiance it floats and by which it is illuminated and made visible, so is all created being in relation to God, but infinitely less. That is what all great spiritual leaders have seen but none have been able to express. There is no language for expressing it!

One gallant try was made by the Lady Julian of Norwich, the medieval anchoress of this diocese, in her "showings" or revelations of Divine Love, which were intellectual visions presented in symbolic pictorial form of poetic imagery.

"He showed me a little thing" she says, "the quantity of an hazel-nut, in the palm of my hand; and it was as round as a ball I looked thereupon with eye of my understanding, and thought, What may this be? And it was answered generally thus. It is all that is made. I marvelled how it might last, for methought it might suddenly have fallen to naught for littleness. And I was answered in my understanding. It lasteth, and ever shall, for that God loveth it. And so All-Thing hath the being by the love of God.

In this Little Thing I saw three properties. The first is that God made it, the second is that God loveth it, the third is that God keepeth it."

This is the truth about all created being as it really is. God made it, God loves it, God keeps it—and it is in relation to Him as a thing of naught.

"Lord, what is man that thou art mindful of him", the psalmist cries, "and the son of man that thou regardest him? Man is like a thing of naught; his time passeth away like a shadow".

Into this thing of naught that He has Himself created, as the poet creates the poem and the musician the melody; which utterly depends on Him but He in no way on it, for in comparison with His Divine Glory that is "set above the heavens" it is nothing and nothing and less than the uttermost nothingness of all nothing—into this very little thing God has Himself entered, by reducing the whole content of His Divine Glory to the unbelievably small scale of one individual human life—one human person in whom, as S. Paul says, "there dwells all the fullness of the Godhead in bodily form" (Col. 2, 9). All the infinite Perfection of the Divine Being which cannot be described in the language of man, except in negative terms—we can only say what God is not, but never what He *is*, for He is far beyond anything we can ever say— all that Perfection of Divine Glory is embodied in the single human person, Jesus Christ, in a way that is hidden from the natural mind of man, and only to be apprehended by the eye of *faith*. "Who being in the form of God, thought it not a prize to be equal with God, but emptied himself out (laid aside his Divine Glory) and took upon him the form of a slave and was made in the likeness of men: and being found in fashion as a man he humbled himself and became obedient unto death, even the death of the cross". (Phil. 2, 5 ff.) That is the mystery of the Incarnation, which cannot be apprehended by the intellect of man, for "the love of Christ surpasseth (human) knowledge", but can only be approached in humility and love, and apprehended by the divinely infused gift of Wisdom—a gift of the Spirit that "comes down from above" and is implanted to the childlike and humble in heart; for "blessed are

* See also e.g. Dom Augustine Morris's sermon p. 52.

the pure in heart, but *they* shall see God".

And Mary is the channel by which He comes into the world. "Behold, the handmaid of the Lord: be it unto me according to thy word". She is Theotokos—the God-Bearer—the title accorded her at the Council of Ephesus of 431, the third Ecumenical (i.e., world-wide) Council of the early Church: this term is roughly translated into Latin as "Dei Genetrix" and into English as "Mother of God". Mary is the God-Bearer, Mother of Him who is essentially God. "The Holy Ghost shall come upon thee, and the power of the highest shall overshadow thee: therefore that which shall be born of thee shall be called holy—Son of God". (S. Luke I, 35). As the channel of the Incarnation— the medium through which it occurs, she is to be rightly hailed as the "Mediatrix of all graces"—though not perhaps in the way propounded by a modern school of Roman theology—for without her the In-carnation and all that springs from it would not have taken place, at least in the way in which it has actually oc-curred. We shall not, therefore, be sur-prised at the tremendous veneration accorded to Mary, the Mother of Jesus, throughout the history of the Church— always in proper relationship to Her Di-vine Son—so that the honour accorded to her redounds to His Glory, for He is greater than she.

The devotion to Mary has been a characteristic mark of the Orthodox Church from the earliest times. "One sound will be heard echoing insistently throughout Orthodox worship", says R. M. French in his book on Orthodoxy, "and that is the praise of the Mother of God. The Theotokos, the God-bearer in her purity, her humility, and the glory of her destiny, is a theme of which Ortho-dox worship never tires. It reaches its climax in the Akathist hymn, which is sung either in part or wholly once a week during the first five weeks of Lent." It is said to have been composed by the Patriarch Sergius in 626 A.D., as a thanksgiving for the deliverance of the city of Byzantium from attack by its ene-mies. The word Akathistos, applied to a hymn, means a hymn you don't sit down for, but, unlike other hymns for which people sit down, all remain standing in token of the honour that is being paid. Here is a quotation from the final stanzas of that hymn:

Praising thy childbearing, we all exalt thee as a living temple, O Mother of God, for in thy womb dwelt He who holdeth all things in His hand, the Lord. He hallowed thee, he glorified thee, he taught all to sing to thee . . . O Mother worthy of all praise, who gavest birth to the Word, most holy above all saints! Accept our present offer-ing, protect us all from every evil, and de-liver from impending doom those who cry together, Alleluia.

I read that recently in Boston, Massachusetts, the Roman Archbishop of Boston addressed some 25,000 people at a World Sodality Day. The pro-gramme was designed as a gesture of friendliness towards Eastern Christians, particularly the Orthodox, many of whom were in attendance. Icons from local Orthodox Churches were dis-played, with special emphasis given to the Vladimir Mother of God, a 12th cen-tury Russian icon now preserved in the Kremlin. The Akathistos hymn was re-cited antiphonally, and a living Rosary was formed, the five mysteries being re-cited in Arabic, Greek, Armenian, Rus-sian and English. The Cardinal said that the presence of both Catholics and Orthodox at services honouring the Vir-gin Mary proved that there was a desire for greater love and understanding among separated Christians. "Mary", he said, "offers great hope of reconcili-ation. We cannot separate the Son from the Mother, nor have the millions of Eastern Orthodox done this any more than we. The *shared love* of the Mother of God may be a link that will bring union to Catholics and Orthodox".

Let us hope that this applies not only to Roman Catholics and Orthodox, but to Anglicans as well, and that the "shared love of the Mother of God" may bring us *all* together in unity of heart and mind. For was not this country once called "the dowry of Mary"? And are there not frescoes of her Assumption into Heaven on the walls of our ancient parish churches and cathedrals? And is there not here in Walsingham itself an Orthodox Chapel right inside our own Shrine Church, and the Roman Slipper Chapel no great distance off? And have we not now in the hymns we still sing ample expression of our devotion to Mary, Mother of Him who is truly God?

Shall we not love thee, Mother dear,
Whom Jesus loved so well,
And to His glory, year by year,
Thy joy and honour tell?

That is a hymn from *Ancient and Modern* that Anglicans of every type, even the most evangelical, will gladly and warmly sing; and its whole emphasis is on the Motherhood of Mary, the Theotokos.

Again, in the *English Hymnal*, 213:
Hail, O Star that pointest
Towards the port of Heaven,
Thou to whom as maiden
God for Son was given.
So, as now we journey,
Aid our weak endeavour,
Till we gaze on Jesus,
And rejoice for ever.

Or, 215:
O glorious Maid, exalted far,
Beyond the light of burning star,
From him who made thee thou has won
Grace to be Mother of his Son.
Thou wast the gate of heaven's high Lord,
The door through which the light hath poured.
Christians rejoice, for through a Maid,
To all mankind is light conveyed!

And in *E.H.* 217, Bishop Ken tells us:
Heaven with transcendant joys her entrance graced,
Next to his throne her Son His Mother placed;
And here below, now she's of heaven possest,
All generations are to call her blest.

Bishop, Ken, the 18th century Non-Juror, who was previously Bishop of Bath and Wells, at least was quite convinced that now in Heaven she fully participates in all the Glory of her own Divine Son: for whom would the King delight to honour more than His very own Mother?

Mary the Dawn,
But Christ the perfect Day;
Mary the Gate,
But Christ the Heavenly Way;
Mary the Root,
But Christ is the Mystic Vine;
Mary the Grape,
But Christ the Sacred Wine;
Mary the Corn-Sheaf,
Christ the Living Bread;
Mary the Rose-Tree,
Christ the Rose, blood-red;
Mary the Fount,
But Christ the Cleansing Flood;
Mary the Chalice,
Christ the Saving Blood;
Mary the Temple,
Christ the Temple's Lord;
Mary the Shrine,
But Christ its God adored;
Mary the Beacon,
Christ the Haven's Rest;
Mary the Mirror,
Christ the Vision Blest.

That is how Mary the God-Bearer stands in respect of Her Divine Son; and we must love and honour her in true relationship to Him. So let us join with our Roman and Orthodox brethren and all other Christian brethren who are united with us by our common baptism into the one great Body of Christ and say:-

Hail Mary, full of grace,
The Lord is with Thee.
Blessed art thou among women
And blessed is the fruit of thy womb, Jesus.
Holy Mary,
Mother of God,
Pray for us sinners, now, and in the hour of our death.   Amen.
Pray for us, O holy Mother of God,
That we may be made worthy of the promises of Christ.

With the help of her prayers, may we all come to be with her in the Glory of Heaven.

Ecumenical Meeting to Discuss Co-operation at Walsingham

An historic meeting took place on 14 March 1968 at the Grail Centre in Sloane Street. It was under the auspices of the new Ecumenical Society of the Blessed Virgin Mary* and the Chairman was the Roman Catholic Bishop of Northampton, Alan Clark. Various people who have an interest in Walsingham had been invited and sixty or seventy people turned up, almost exactly half Roman Catholics and half Anglicans. The Bishop opened with prayer and Mr. Gillett, the Organizing Secretary, welcomed those who had come and gave an introduction in which he hoped that the "unhappy rivalry" which had gone on from time to time since the restoration of devotion to Our Lady of Walsingham could be gradually obliterated in the warmth of a new understanding and appreciation of each other. The Bishop then opened with a few words in which he said that at the Reformation there had been a breakdown in charity and also a breakdown in dogmatic agreement; it was the breakdown in charity which we were seeking to heal and when we could speak to each other in love the doctrinal differences would appear in a new light.

The first item for discussion was "The need for Ecumenical Co-operation between the two Shrines in Walsingham in honour of Our Lady and consideration of the legitimate extent of such co-operation". This was introduced by Fr. Stephenson and Fr. Connelly, S.M., the new priest-in-charge of the Slipper Chapel. Fr. Stephenson said that Anglicans desired to share whatever they had at Walsingham with their Roman brethren. He also said that, although he knew there had been unhappy incidents in the past, during the ten years he had been at Walsingham nothing could have been happier or more friendly than relations with Roman Catholics who lived and worked there. Fr. Connelly echoed the desire for closer co-operation and hoped that we might find ways of helping each other.

In the discussion a direct question was asked as to how far Roman Catholics could take part in Anglican pilgrimages. The Bishop said that they were bound by the regulations issued by the English hierarchy, which meant that they could join in any worship with other Christians except Eucharistic worship. However he was empowered to give special permission for special occasions and this he would gladly do in the case of Walsingham. Fr. Brewer next spoke about bringing a party of Anglicans on the Roman National Pilgrimage in August and he said that the great sadness was that they had to separate for the Eucharist, and it was felt by all present that this was something which ought to bring home to us in a very vivid way the horror of our disunity.

Mr. Arthur Bond spoke and so did Fr. Roe, and Fr. Harris who lives at the Slipper Chapel. Fr. Roe said that the Parish Church was always available to pilgrims of any denomination with the understanding that he needed the concurrence of the Bishop of Norwich. Fr. Harris spoke of his "ministry of the garden wall" over which he spoke to visitors of all shades of belief or none at all during the summer months while pruning the roses. Speakers representing the Union of Catholic Mothers, the All-Night Vigil Movement, the Ecumenical Schools pilgrimage and the Student Cross, all spoke. One used the phrase "The Conversion of England" and then added "I suppose we ought not to use that phrase these days", to which the Bishop reponded "we still pray for the Conversion of England, the only difference is that these days we include ourselves!"

---

* Founded by Martin Gillett, a frequent pilgrim to Walsingham, whose ashes are immured in the Slipper Chapel.

It was agreed that we should encourage parishes coming on pilgrimage to join with their neighbours either Anglican or Roman Catholic, and the same was true of identical Societies in each Church. There were further speeches by Mother Elizabeth, S.S.M., and Stanley Smith about combining the facilities of hospitality and letting each other know of dates and arrangements for pilgrimages so that we may make full use of our respective "plants".

One very practical result of the meeting was the decision that when we had exhausted the existing supply of literature, we would prepare a brochure to serve pilgrims of both Shrines and try and obliterate for the casual visitor any sense of rivalry.

The Bishop said that should it be possible at any time to acquire the Abbey grounds, Roman Catholics would not wish to do so for themselves alone, but only in conjunction with their Anglican brethren.

Fr. Stephenson said that he knew that none of the Anglicans present would wish such a meeting to end without some mention being made of the name of Alfred Hope Patten to whom, under God, they owed everything that they had at Walsingham.

Canon Donald Nicholson proposed a vote of thanks to the Bishop who gave those present his blessing.

Fr. Stephenson and Fr. Connelly were entrusted with the task of forming a permanent Committee to promote co-operation at Walsingham. Perhaps nothing very sensational was decided and certainly those present were very conscious that we have a long way to go, but Our Lady is Queen of Peace and we are all conscious that at Walsingham she bestows her favours irrespective of place or denomination, and this gives us the confidence to go forward in faith.

The first Anglican-Roman Catholic Commission, established as a result of the historic meeting in Rome of Archbishop Michael Ramsey with Pope Paul VI in 1966, had already produced the three joint statements which were overwhelmingly endorsed by the 1988 Lambeth Conference, when the R.C. Co-Chairman, Alan Clark, then Bishop of East Anglia, preached at the National Pilgrimage in 1979.

My Brethren,

Walsingham, to which you have come today in such great numbers and in a spirit of devotion to Mary, Mother of God, is a place of secrets. These secrets are the most precious of all the secrets of the human heart. It is a place where Simeon's prophetic words find fulfilment. Because Mary's own heart was pierced by the terrible sword of sorrow, the thoughts of our own hearts, past memories and present anguish, find it easier to come to the surface of our consciousness and are woven into our prayer. The barriers that seemed to hold them in check fall away and, in Mary's domain, we stand before God, with no attempt to conceal the truth of our need. Here the terror of hidden fears is somehow dissipated and we sense healing in the depths of our spirit. And all this because we come in prayer and praise to be in the company of one who was and remains the first disciple of the new people of God, ransomed and redeemed by the love of her own Son.

The secret of Walsingham is that it is a secret resting place for each and every pilgrim—for the pilgrim who comes tired and weary, for the pilgrim brimming over with eagerness and joy, for the reluctant pilgrim who is not without doubt or perplexity, even for the pilgrim who cannot conceal his or her hostility whose cries are mixed with the terrible questioning that goes with inexplicable sadness. For, through the grace of her beloved Son, Walsingham will always be a place for healing, a place of prayer, a place of refreshment. How we should thank God that we are united in gratitude for the gift of Christ's Mother, given to us when, in the eyes of the world, the Gospel had utterly failed as Jesus, her Son, gave up his spirit on the Cross. Our coming is itself a celebration in prayer and praise, in liturgy and sacrament, of the Son who gave us his Mother. Though the privacies of our thoughts and feelings are still with us, it is as a family and as a community that we sing and pray. To be a pilgrim to Walsingham carries its own reward.

Of course, Walsingham has its open secrets. It remains a choice of Mary. Its desolation, through destruction and abandonment, in no way changed its profile—that it should be always England's Nazareth. Hence the pretentious and the sophisticated will need, like the rich, a very low crouch if they are to enter into its humble mystery. It is the poor who have the Gospel preached to them in this sacred place—those whose daily life runs in ordinary patterns, in the so-called normal circumstances of human living, who may have enough but with nothing over for what the world calls fulfilling and exciting, whose poverty is as much within as without—poverty of mind, of feeling, of devotion. This is the meeting place of the humble and the sinner as much as of the holy and generous. Here indeed is a true equality.

Any prayerful reflection on why we have come will include our seeking to understand the mystery of Nazareth where Christ chose to live the major part of his life. If it be true that he needed those thirty years in order to become fully a man—like us in all things but sin—and experience in himself the meaning of his own incarnation in human history, then it is equally true that the Nazareth of Walsingham can disclose to us its secret: that the pilgrim way for the Christian is to be found in the ordinary

and unpretentious and that it is within these unprepossessing circumstances that we are called to be holy and faithful. Walsingham contains treasures of the Gospel—for those who come from the highways and byways are privileged guests, all being invited, there are no favourites. Even those who only stand and stare will return home pondering the Word of God in their hearts, hearts pierced by the love that begets repentance, hearts strengthened for daily care, hearts exposing their sorrow to other hearts equally downcast with personal failure, hearts suddenly warm with the experience of being loved by so good a God, so loving a Brother, so endearing a Mother.

Yes, all these human things are here. The spirit has room to breathe. No one will leave this hidden place without the springs of renewal in their inmost soul.

But does no one here today question why this should be so? Is it not enough for us to accept, some may say, that all this must be so if Mary is Mother of Jesus and, by his express command, Mother of us all? The mystery of Mary's universal motherhood is more than enough to explain all. The pilgrim heart finds warmth and comfort enough in the company of so loving a Mother. Do not these precious words of Pope Paul VI say all:

> "To modern man, the blessed Virgin Mary . . . offers a serene vision, and a reassuring word: the victory of hope over anguish, of communion over solitude, of peace over agitation, of joy and beauty over boredom and nausea, of life over death."

The truth and beauty of these words are in no wise lessened if I dare to say that they are but an introduction—and a necessary one—to a growth in understanding of Mary's place in the economy of salvation, a growth that must be nurtured and fostered and, can I say, compelled and forced if we are to be soon one pilgrim people, undivided in our mission to today's world where starvation of the spirit is more rampant than the hunger and famine of the oppressed and weak. It is the hour to come out of our privacy and go into the public glare of the market place prophetically sited in the miserable town of Nazareth. For Nazareth is not far from Capernaum where Christ taught the essentials of the Gospel. We accept that we are solemnly pledged to a unity not yet attained, that we fail before God by our inability to preach in indivisibility the one faith of our baptism. Our very poverty traps us into dissipating precious energy in maintaining controversies which should long ago have been absorbed into new and mutual understandings. Lord, forgive us when we mistakenly stand firm when we should yield and yield when we should stand firm.

These generalisations, I fear, may well bear little fruit if they cannot be reduced to the world of the real and the particular—the world of our own experience. For God, who is the summit of reality, speaks to real people, as real as you and me. And our Christian vocation is real and particular for each of us. Yet we know, with equal certainty, that we cannot respond to the demands of this vocation on our own: we are compelled to come out of our privacy and open ourselves to one another in community—for salvation is located in that community which Jesus Christ founded and continues, in the Spirit, to found, which we call 'the Church'. God's covenant with man in the person of Jesus Christ must be expressed not so much in words as in people who hear the Word and keep it. Such people, and only such people, are true disciples of the Lord. Hence the great question stands before us: are we worthy to be called disciples of the Lord?

This is not a speculative question. Though deeply theological in its implications, it requires a personal answer. Today's pilgrimage will inevitably and inexorably force from our hearts—too often hearts of stone rather than of flesh— a longing to respond with the same kind of unqualified 'yes' that came from Our Lady's lips at the Annunciation. Our personal resources may be small and meagre—hence our need for daily grace to utter an answer that completely outstrips those resources.

So, unabashed by the audacity which the words betray, I would ask you to turn for help to the one who, poor and humble though she was, was yet unafraid to accept the Word of God in a spirit of complete obedience. It is time for all of us to look again, lovingly and courageously, at Mary, the first of Christ's disciples, the first and most honoured member of the new people of God, the pride of the redeemed race of man. Looking at her, we remember that, even as we ourselves, she needed to be redeemed—even though she received this redemption from the omnipotent hand of God in such a way that from the first she was fully open to the grace of discipleship and thus was and remains *the* example of what it means to be a true disciple of the Lord. In words rich in beauty and meaning, she has been called 'the beginning of the better world' (Paul VI).

Here, I venture to say, is the deeply doctrinal lesson behind the Marian piety we profess. If it is time to forget sterile controversies, it is also time to sweep aside the distortions of that piety. In a spirit of simplicity we need to recover a feeling of wonder that centuries of Christian tradition have spoken of her as the type of the Church. We must ask why this should be so, what does it mean, how does it change my own attitudes and enrich my own understanding of what I should be. By calling Mary the type of the Church, we are saying that we can discover in her what is required of those who claim to follow Jesus in true discipleship. Her response at the Annunciation: "May it be done unto me according to your word" is the key to all understanding of God's loving covenant with men and women of all time. This covenant, this Word, governs all—the personal and the universal—so that the Church can be described as the community which hears the Word of God and keeps it. Far from disowning her when he called us—through our keeping of that Word, his mother, sister and brother—Jesus tenderly acknowledged Mary was the first to hear the Word and accept it in the obedience of faith. As Augustine said so perceptively of her: Mary first conceived the Word of God in her heart before she conceived him in her body. Mary thus offers to us the reality of true discipleship and provokes from our searching hearts praise and thanksgiving that, because of that obedience, there is the Church, there is the family of God in Christ. "Those who wish to be called by the Christian name", a modern writer has said, "will only be brought into that one family if they are able to recognise in Mary's life the pattern of their own".

The secret is out. It is the secret of Nazareth. It is the secret of Walsingham. Pondered over in prayerful simplicity, it can remove mountains of misunderstanding. To enter into the secrecy of its hiddenness we need pure eyes and clean hearts. There can be no pretences in those who humbly listen and, equally humbly, try to do the Word of God. I say it is a Nazareth secret, for she accepted its demands in the very ordinary, so-called normal circumstances of a poor and unpretentious life. Yet in living that life she shared with her Son, over long years, danger, poverty, rejection, frustration. It was in Nazareth that she learnt the patience and compassion that would bring her to the foot of the Cross. Hers was a continuing growth in holiness, hers was a daily deepening of prayer and acceptance of the divine will. Hers was the hope that was crowned, after her Son's Resurrection, by the privilege of entering into the presence of God for all eternity in her full humanity. She is the faithful daughter of Sion. As Pope John Paul said recently:

"Mary is the fullest expression of perfect faithfulness to the Holy Spirit and to his action in the soul: she is the expression of the faithfulness which means persevering co-operation in the grace of our vocation."

There is more to be said—but it must be said swiftly and briefly, for it is really only saying again something of the secret of Walsingham. All who see their own faith in Mary's, believing as she believed, acting out that faith in their own lives, will certainly be made one. The weeds of confrontation and difference will be choked out of existence by our accepting together the personal dedication to the Word of God which is the hallmark of the sanctity which is Mary's. One of the great writers of modern times gives us reassurance:

"It is not our part to master all the tides of the world, but to do what is in us for the succour of those years in which we are set, uprooting the evils in the fields that we know, so that those who live after may have clear earth to till."

(The Lord of the Rings)

If Mary's task was unique, so is ours. For we are uniquely loved and uniquely graced. No one will do exactly the same thing, no one will phrase the Gospel message in exactly the same words. But all of us find a unity precisely in the pursuit of the unity we have lost and are now re-discovering. My presence here today, in response to so gracious an invitation as I received, is a sign and pledge of this. We have the lesson to learn of true discipleship where there is no room to serve two masters, where the greatest must be as the smallest, where all is gift and the merit belongs to the giver more than the receiver. As yet, we are learners in the art of discipleship and must continue to look on her who learnt that art to the greatest possibility open to her. It is time to clear the earth and rid it of the weeds and tares of our own manufacture.

Let us then ask, with confidence, for the graces we need that are hidden in the secret storehouse of Walsingham. When we return home to our congregations and communities, let us—like the disciples who gathered to pray round the Mother of the Lord—devote our energies to equipping ourselves to walk the path of unity. To step on to that road is a hazardous thing and demands a persevering faith and an enduring hope. There are many dangers on that road, for one is not permitted to halt and rest awhile. Christ leads us and his Mother encourages us. "Whatever he shall say to you, do ye". In a terrible way, the future of the world is put into our hands, and we might well despair did we not hear those precious words: "I am with you always, even to the end of the world". But our vision sees the beckoning hand of Mary who trusted the Word of God and obeyed it without reserve.

If her Son prays for the unity of his brethren, whom he has committed to the care of his Mother, how can we turn our eyes away from her who has never ceased to point to him as the one and only Saviour of all mankind? It is in our prayerful reflection on 'the family connection', that we will discover the greatest secret of all the secrets of Walsingham—that, by the grace of her Son, she engenders, as only a Mother can, brethren of one faith and disciples of unity.

When the Archbishop of Canterbury came to preach at the National Pilgrimage in 1980, he visited the Slipper Chapel to pray for unity.

159

The Golden Jubilee of the re-building of the Shrine was acknowledged by messages from Rome and Westminster.

VATICAN CITY—WEDNESDAY 14TH OCTOBER 1981

His Holiness Pope John Paul II has been informed of the Golden Jubilee celebrations at the Anglican Shrine at Walsingham and he would ask you to convey his cordial greetings. It is the prayer of His Holiness that Walsingham will ever be a centre for well ordered and fruitful dialogue undertaken and sustained with openness to the promptings of the spirit of truth so that he may hasten the day when full unity in faith is finally attained.

CARDINAL CASAROLI

LAMBETH PALACE SE1 7JU

During the last 50 years the Shrine buildings have been a place where many pilgrims have found refreshment and inspiration in their Christian pilgrimage. I well remember my own visit last year, and the other occasions when I have found inspiration and encouragement for my ministry at this Shrine of Our Lady.

I assure you of my support and prayers for your Golden Jubilee and for the future.

ROBERT CANTUAR

ARCHBISHOP'S HOUSE WESTMINSTER LONDON SW1P 1QJ

I am happy to send my prayers and good wishes to the Anglican Shrine of Our Lady of Walsingham on the occasion of its Golden Jubilee.

Walsingham meant so much to our English ancestors and, since its revival in this century, Anglicans, Roman Catholics and other Christians have visited it in ever growing numbers. Our Lady is finding a place in the hearts of more and more Christians. We ask her to bring "England, her Dowry" back to the knowledge, love and service of her divine Son and to re-unite us all in Him.

BASIL HUME
Cardinal Archbishop of Westminster

When Pope John Paul II came to Britain in 1982, he could not pay his customary visit to the national shrine of our Lady. So a statue of O.L.W. was taken to the papal mass at Wembley by Fr. Birch and Fr Colven together.

The statue of O.L.W. on the altar, at the Pope's request, for his Mass before 80,000 pilgrims in May 1982.

161

In the same year Father Colven was invited to preach at a televised service at the R.C. Shrine in the new Chapel of Reconciliation. Alluding to the mass at Wembley, he said:

As the Pope spoke he was interrupted by bursts of applause, and it was noticeable that the clapping was at its loudest when he spoke about Christian unity. In our own generation, there has been a fundamental change in the attitude of Christians to one another. The days of competition are over, and we can look at our different traditions with fresh eyes.

Sixty years ago when the Vicar of Walsingham, Alfred Hope Patten, began to revive the ancient devotion of Our Lady in this village there was controversy. Some Roman Catholics resented what he was doing, while there were Anglicans who thought it was very strange and un-English. Happily, this is no longer the case and we are here together this morning in this modern building—fittingly dedicated as the chapel of Reconciliation—we are Anglicans and Roman Catholics and other Christians worshipping together with the Mother of Jesus as the theme of our service. Instead of being the point of division, Mary has become a focus for unity and we thank God for this change in attitude.

Archbishop Barbarito, the Papal Pro-Nuncio to Great Britain, led an R.C. pilgrimage to Walsingham on June 28th, 1987. He is photographed here with the Administrator, Father Fellows beside the effigy of Father Hope Patten when he visited the shrine church and offered prayers in the Holy House for Christian unity.

MASTER OF THE GUARDIANS

Alfred Hope Patten	1931–58
John Colin Stephenson	1958–73
Arthur John Colin Burke Gill	1973–82
David Michael Hope	1982–

ADMINISTRATOR OF THE SHRINE

Alfred Hope Patten	1931–58
John Colin Stephenson	1958–73
Charles David Smith	1968–72
Alan Vincent Carefull	1973–81
Christopher George Colven	1981–86
Roy Fellows	1987–

PARISH PRIEST OF WALSINGHAM

Alfred Hope Patten	1921–58
Alan Arthur Roe	1959–77
John Edgar Barnes	1977–89
Michael John Rear	1989–

Short Bibliography

H.M. Gillett *Walsingham. The History of a famous Shrine* (2nd edition 1950)

A. Hope Patten *Mary's Shrine of the Holy House, Walsingham* Cambridge 1954

J.C. Dickinson *The Shrine of Our Lady of Walsingham* Cambridge 1956

Charles Green & A.B. Whittingham 'Excavations at Walsingham Priory 1961'
Archaeological Journal vol 125 (1968) pp 255–90

J.C. Stephenson *Walsingham Way* 1970

J.C. Stephenson *Merrily on High* 1972

Brian Spencer *Medieval Pilgrim Badges from Norfolk* Norfolk Museum Service 1980

Claude Fisher *Walsingham. A Place of Pilgrimage for all People* Walsingham 1983

Donald Hole & others *Walsingham. England's Nazareth* new edition 1985

Heather M. Beaumont *Sir William Milner* (1985)

Arthur Bond *The Walsingham Story* new edition Walsingham 1988

Sources

p4 W. Reany *The Shrine of OLW* 1939 p43 Archbishop's Letter *Review* 71 (1980).

p5 Photo of AHP. C. Stephenson *Walsingham Way* Frontispiece. How AHP came to Walsingham *Our Lady's Mirror* Spring 1946.

p6 M Gudgeon. 'Buxted' *Review* 77 (1982)

p7 A. Bond 'First Impressions' *Review* 38 (1971).
  Fr Derrick Lingwood Remembers *Mirror* Autumn 1958/Winter 1959.

p10, 13 Photos of AHP *Review* 80 (1983) *Mirror* Autumn 1956.

p14 Sir William Milner's Reminiscences *Mirror* Autumn 1958/Winter 1959.

p18 Stanley Smith on death of AHP *Review* 38 (1971).

p19 AHP 'Walsingham Friary' *Mirror* Summer 1948; Drawing of EMC *England's National Shrine of Our Lady* p6.

p23 Colin Stephenson 'On writing about Fr Hope Patten' *Review* 36 (1970).

p25 AHP 'The Story of the Shrine 1922–1947' *Mirror* Spring/Summer 1947

p27 Photo of O'Rorke: Archives.

p28 AHP Account of restoration of Shrine & ground plan *Sanctuary of OLW described by Erasmus* (1931) p14f; Account of Stations *'The Little Guide' to the Sanctuary of OLW* 3rd edition 1935, of alterations *Mirror* Summer 1938.

p29 Shrine of OLW in Parish Church: Archives.

p31f. drawings by EMC *England's National Shrine*.

p32 Account of opening of Shrine 1931 Hole/Stephenson/Colven *Walsingham* [*Mirror* Autumn 1931] Photos: *Mary's Shrine* p25, and Archives.

p35 Fr Baverstock's Sermon *Mirror* Autumn 1936

p37 Shrine Bells *Mirror* Autumn 1936. Account of blessing of extension of Shrine 1938, *Mary's Shrine* p42 photo: Archives

p39 Fr Biggart's Sermon 1938 *Church Times* 10 June 1938

p42 Bernard Craze *Review* 52 (1974).

p43 Plan *Mary's Shrine* p32.

p44 Stones of High Altar *Mirror* Summer 1943; Information from *Mirror* Winter 1932, Winter 1934, Spring & Summer 1936, *Little Guide* & Stephenson p163, 193.

p46 H. J. Fynes-Clinton 'Armorial Bearings of our Lady' *Mirror* Spring 1945. Photo of Holy House *Mary's Shrine* p40.

p48 'London Committee for Walsingham' *Review* 9 (1963).
  Photo of image *Mary's Shrine* p88.

p49 'Walsingham Jubilee' *Mirror* Autumn 1956

p52 Abbot of Nashdom's Sermon 1956 *Mirror* Autumn 1956.

p54 Anthony Symondson 'Victorian Architects' *Review* 63 (1977)

p57 Conclusion of Centenary Year 1961 *Review* 3 (1961)

p58 Drawing by EMC *Review* 17 (1965).

p59 Photo *Review* 43 (1972).

p59–63 Golden Jubilee 1981; Photo & Bishop of London's sermon *Review* 75 (1981).

p64 Photo of cutting of first sod of S. Josephs: K. Faircloth Photo of opening *Review* 87 (1985).

p65 Account of first pilgrimage *Pilgrim's Almanac* 1928

p66 Programme Original in ms. copy of Feasey on Walsingham.

p67 Account of second pilgrimage May 1923 *Church Times* 25 May Photo: Archives

p69 Account of Centenary Pilgrimage Hole.

p70 Photo Walsingham Pilgrimage [1935]. Pilgrim Hymn. *Pilgrim's Manual* 1928. A further revision was suggested in *Review* 87 (1985).

p73 G. D. Carleton The Intention of a Pilgrim *Mirror* Autumn/Winter 1947/8.

p75 EMC Poem *Mirror* Spring 1946.

p76–7 S. J. Forrest Poems *Mirror* Autumn 1948; *Review* 12 (1964).

p78 Kathleen Blayney. Those were the Days *Review* 63 (1977). Photo: Archives.

p81 Anon priest *Review* 22 (1966) Enid Chadwick *Review* 75 (1981).

p83 National Pilgrimage 1959: cutting from an unidentified paper in archives.

p84 Photo: Lynn News & Advertiser.

p85 First Ecumenical Pilgrimage *Review* 37 (1970) . . . Parliamentary *Review* 47 (1973).

p86 Guardians *Review* 72 (1980) Photo: *Mirror* Autumn 1955.

p87 C. D. Smith 'Colin Stephenson' *Review* 49 (1973) Photo: *Mirror* Autumn 1958/Winter 1959.

p90 Lauderdale 'Colin Gill' *Review* 76 (1982)

p92 C. D. Smith 'Jack Banson' *Review* 67 (1979);

p93 Fr Alban Baverstock AHP *Mirror* Summer 1950.

p94 Fr Francis Baverstock *Mirror* Autumn 1952 Martin Gibbs "Walter Gervase Bennett" *Review* 60 (1976).

p95 C.H. Nixon 'Sir John Best-Shaw' *Review* 83 (1984); Photo: Archives.

p97 Major Bowker *Mirror* Summer 1950.

Ivan Young 'Fr Fynes-Clinton' *Occasional Paper 9* (May 1960), abridged from *Messenger of the Catholic League* Jan–April 1960. Photo: Archives

p98 PhilipHusbands *Review* 93 (1987);

p99 Mervyn Stockwood 'Uvedale Lambert' *Review* 81 (1983).

p100 Stanley Smith 'Derrick Lingwood' *Review* 43 (1972) Photo: S. Smith.

p102 Patrick Maitland 'Sir William Milner' *Occasional Paper* 10 (Sept 1960) (from *Church Times* 8 April 1960) Photo: Archives.

p104 E.H.W. Crusha 'Hubert Adderley, Lord Norton' *Occasional Paper* 12 (March 1961);

p105 Canon Peterson *Review* 20 (1966).

Arthur Smallwood *Mirror* Winter/Spring 1938.

p106 William Mason 'John Twisaday' *Review* 38 (1971).

p107 Fr Whitby *Mirror* Autumn 1948

p108 Order of OLW *Review* 72 (1980).

p109 C.D. Smith 'Enid Chadwick' *Review* 93 (1987) Photo: Archives.

p111 Anon. 'Dorothy Ferrier' *Review* 46 (1973);

p112 'Lawrence Harding' *Review* 74 (1981);

p113 Bp Ambrose Weekes 'Laurence King' *Review* 76 (1982).

'Margaret O'Ferrall' *Review* 73 (1981);

p114 David Baker 'Michael Smith' *Review* 62 (1977);

p115 Photo K. Faircloth. Stanley Smith 'Leonard Whitmore *Review* 86 (1985)

p116 Alice England *Mirror*. Summer 1945.

'William Frary' *Mirror* Summer 1953

p117 'Alex Lawson' *Review* 20 (1966).

p118 The Sisters *Review* 23 (1967) SSM & photo *Review* 79 (1983).

p119 'Mother Margaret Mary SSM' *Review* 32 (1969).

p121 AHP on C.S.A. *Mirror* Summer 1948, Spring/Summer 1958.

p122 Photos *Mary's Shrine* p56 [= *Mirror* Autumn 1945].

p123 Leslie Oldroyd 'Life in the College. . .' *Review* 65 & 66 (1978) Photo (K Faircloth) *Mirror* Spring/Summer 1958.

p127 Photo of Refectory: Archives.

p128 EMC drawing *Mirror* Summer 1953

p129 Fr Forrest's sermon 1956 *Mirror* Autumn 1956.

p133 Bp. Stockwood's sermon *Review* 17 (1965).

p136 Bp. Patrick Rodger *Review* 59 (1976).

p138 Bp. Ramsey *Review* 65 (1978).

p140 Abp Runcie *Review* 71 (1980).

p142 Bp Bavin *Review* 92 (1987).

p145 Sara Maitland *Review* 73 (1981).

p147 AHP on reunion *Mirror* Spring 1945; Anon. 'Mary & Prayer for Unity' *Mirror*
        Summer 1953.

p150 J.C. Stephenson & visit to Pope John XXIII *Occasional Paper* 12 (March 1961)

p151 Fr Dalby's sermon *Review* 2 (1961).

p154 Ecumenical meeting *Review* 28 (1968)

p155 Bp Alan Clark's sermon *Review* 68 (1979).

p159 Photo Claude Fisher *Walsingham. A Place of Pilgrimage. . .* (1983)

p160 Messages 1981 *Review* 75 (1981).

p161 Photos. Claude Fisher *Walsingham. . .* (1983)
        Photo Abp. Barbarito *Review* 92 (1987)

p162 Fr Colven's Sermon *Review* 78 (1982).